Living with LONDON MIDLAND LOCOMOTIVES

Living with LONDON MIDLAND LOCOMOTIVES

A. J. Powell

LONDON

IAN ALLAN LTD

First published 1977

ISBN 0 7110 0728 4

Published by Ian Allan Ltd, Shepperton, Surrey,
and printed in the United Kingdom by
Ian Allan Printing Ltd

Contents

Introduction

In 1957, after I had written a letter to the Editor of the *Trains Illustrated* commenting on an article on the 'Royal Scots', I was invited to do a series in the magazine telling something of practical experience with the locomotives with which I was familiar. It was the Editor himself who suggested the title *Living with LM Locomotives*: certainly it so closely matched what, over the years, I had been paid to do that I did not argue about it. Seven of those articles appeared between November 1957 and March 1959, under the pen-name — or number — of '45671'. The disguise fooled few of my friends for long.

This book is based, somewhat loosely, on those writings, together with additional material, both published and otherwise. But it was only when sitting down to write this introduction that the title really struck home and made me ponder just what can be claimed to constitute 'living with locomotives'. And when did one start this lifestyle?

Was it when, as a schoolboy, one began to take a more serious interest in the technicalities, operation and performance of steam locomotives than is associated with the ticking off of numbers in carefully compiled Woolworth notebooks? (This was before the invaluable *ABCs* of Ian Allan). Or was it at some stage after starting an apprenticeship in a works or depot involved in building or repairing locomotives? I say 'at some stage' because the first two years in a works tended to be concerned with machining or fitting components barely recognisable as relevant to a locomotive. Or was it when, basic training completed, one became an adult responsible in some way for designing, or organising the maintenance, or controlling the operations, of a fleet of locomotives?

Perhaps the answer is that this latter stage, particularly when involved with operation and front-line maintenance, is the one at which one truly begins to be living with locomotives, but that everything which has gone before has been noted, filed away and indexed in the mind to provide a database of experience on which to draw, on which to make judgments, on which to set standards of quality. Not least, it is the life-stage at which one really begins to know — or think one knows — how the other fellow's mind is working, what will appeal to him and what he will reject, and to practise the subtle art of influence and guidance to get where one wants to be.

Let me, therefore, dredge my own memories, from watching the West

Coast main line at work in the late 1920s, and 1930s, from earning the scarcely princely wages of an engineering apprentice in the locomotive works at Derby from 1936 to 1941, and then from watching over the operation and repair of steam locomotives on the LMS and LM Region in the post-war years until the decline of steam set in. I shall quote extensively from the original articles, while retaining the freedom which, I hope, greyer hairs permit, to change bits which I would today, with hindsight, give different emphasis or colour. The chapters will not be heavily loaded with logs of runs, but snippets of performance will find a place where they are felt to give an insight into what locomotives — and even more the two men who coaxed the work out of them — could do. It will have a strong design element in it, and I think I may justly claim that it will be authentic.

And finally, since I am no more able to resist the temptation to dream of what might have been than most, I shall appoint myself CME at Derby for a while and set out my own ideas on how the locomotive fleet which has been under scrutiny might have been moulded, better to meet the conditions of post-war operation and perhaps to have avoided the disorderly haste of the late 1950s/early 1960s rush into the arms of Dr. Diesel.

During those often exciting days in the late 1940s and 1950s, I owed a debt of gratitude to many people who helped, guided and encouraged me. Two particular names stand out. E. S. Cox, for whom I worked directly for a number of years, was always ready to listen to me and accept a sound and reasoned case. The late Bill Thorley contributed some of his very wide experience of Motive Power maintenance (which emerges so clearly in his book *A Breath of Steam*) during our numerous trips out together on casualty examinations and studies of depot maintenance; I have been privileged to succeed him as Senior Traction Officer, BR HQ.

Two other people must also be mentioned; firstly my wife, who has patiently accepted the loss of my company during the writing of this book and the preparation of the drawings; and secondly Sara Priday, who has given me unstinted assistance with its typing and coped with my appalling writing.

Back with the clock and calendar, then, to live with LM steam.

1/Boyhood

There was a very strong railway element amongst my forebears, though none reached very exalted rank. My father, a lifelong railwayman, settled in Rugby before World War I and remained there for the rest of his life. Uncles on both sides of the family included a stationmaster (Loughborough LNW), at least one signalman, and others. When I was young, my father was stationmaster's clerk, and before the days of complex fares structures and seat reservations, doubled as enquiry office clerk also. In the mid-1930s he foresook his gloomy, gaslit office at the head of the exit ramps and became chief booking clerk, in an equally gloomy office in the main station building.

Every Wednesday as stationmaster's clerk he was required to work until 7pm, and there was a ritual that I took his sandwiches and a covered jug of tea, stowed in a shopping bag and carried with the utmost care to avoid spillage, the five minute walk to his office at 5 o'clock. This gave some opportunity to see locomotives at close quarters, but he did not encourage me to hang about the platforms. So my acquaintance with LMS trains really concentrated on 'The Block', an entry to a row of railway cottages at the foot of Railway Terrace, almost opposite Rugby No 4 box, and where, if one sat on the stile in the fence, one could reach out and almost touch the LNW G1s and G2s that passed on the Down Goods line. Other desirable observation points were the bottom of South Street, hard by the GC line bridge over the LMS and the famous 44-arm signal gantry, and the dirt lanes alongside the Trent Valley line out towards Newbold troughs.

By the time I was old enough to take notice, the 'Claughtons' were receiving red LMS livery and the Midland Compounds were beginning to appear on the Birmingham two-hour expresses. The first flush of enthusiasm, following the amalgamation, for painting passenger locomotives in crimson lake soon evaporated, however. There were 'Georges' and 'Princes' about so painted, but no more were being done and newly shopped examples appeared in lined black. Occasionally one saw a black engine with a red tender or vice-versa. The 'Claughtons' kept their red livery, however, right to the end.

Was there ever a more beautiful big engine than a 'Claughton'? The large wheel bosses, the long coupling rod splashers, the half-hidden Walschaerts valve gear and the sleek lines of boiler and firebox should

9

have resulted in a magnificently balanced design, if only " handsome does as handsome is" were the rule. We knew in a casual sort of way that all was not well with them, for we saw most of the efforts to improve them — the Caprotti valve gear, first on *Alfred Fletcher* and then on nine others, the big 'G9½S' boilers on 20 of them, the cast iron chimney of the Kylala blastpipe engines — and we heard some starting out of Rugby, hidden by the screen walls, at what sounded like a furious, light engine pace until they emerged conventionally but making eight beats per revolution. But how impressive they looked: the strongly horizontal line of footframing and splashers, the well-set-back smokebox, those smoothly-turning wheels uncluttered by visible balance weights.

Our youthful discussions were carried out against a noise background of squealing flanges as 'Georges' backed into the north end bays. They were no mean engines, even though by that time they had been demoted to semi-fast and local work. Two of them always stood pilot at Rugby, one up-side and one down-side, to take over in case of failure. It was in 1932 that No 5392 *Penmaenmawr* took over the up 'Mancunian' at short notice from a failed 'Royal Scot' and worked the 295ton train to Euston in 84min for the 82.6miles, including 55min for the 59.9miles in from Roade. Not to be despised from a 60-ton 4-4-0 at the ripe old age of 20.

And the 'Princes': what a remarkable noise *they* made. There were invariably two strong beats and two quieter ones — I am not sure which end of the cylinders was doing the lion's share of the work — but usually overlying the strong beats was a loud wheezing noise from leakage at the snifting valves just above the footframing. And the 'Tishy's' with outside Walschaerts valve gear — how they fascinated us.

The names we rolled round our young tongues were rich ones like *Simoom, Bucephalus* and *Gallipoli.* Even the element of doubt about some of the names had its virtue, long before any printed lists or booklets were available generally. This was what made the Midland engines, either Compounds on the main-line trains or others working in off the Leicester branch, so much less interesting. Who could get excited about No 1165 when *Leviathan, Mammoth* or *Sisyphus* were there for the asking? Or, of course, the superb *Patriot* with her extra-large, well-polished nameplate, which was shedded at Rugby, always kept very smart and which took part each year in the Steam Shed Remembrance service?

In the late 1920s and early 1930s the 'Royal Scots' (a number of which were then carrying delightful names of early locomotives) were the mainstay of the West Coast main-line express work, and the hard work and high speeds that constituted their day-to-day performances have been recorded in detail elsewhere. They had their troubles, naturally, but at that time the only one I heard of from first-hand knowledge was the occasional propensity for that high-pitched scream of a whistle to stick open and defy all attempts to get it to shut. I think it was in the early summer of 1934, when I was sitting a mock-School Certificate examination, that the whole of Rugby was regaled for a couple of hours by that continuous whistle; the driver of the up 'Merseyside Express' had sounded it at Rugby No 7, and that was that. Stop on the up through line at the south end of the station; fitter from the adjacent shed to attend to it, without success. There was no alternative but to hook off, on to the shed, drop the fire and wait for the boiler to empty itself.

It was at about this time that I got wind of the impending passage of Mr (later Sir William) Stanier's new 'magnum opus' on its way from Crewe Works to Euston for official inspection. I cut school games that afternoon to see this strange new Pacific, still in works photographic grey paint, when she stopped for about an hour on the up fast line at Rugby. Big, to us then, meant the compact chubbiness of a 'Royal Scot', but here was enormous length, while the smokebox was actually smaller in diameter than that of a 'Scot', permitting quite a respectable chimney. But oh, how wrong that tender looked — a poor thing, the original 4,000gallon version of the Midland tender. The whole ensemble seemed rather ungainly, and needed a period of mental adjustment to get used to.

From time to time we felt a need to leaven our diet of LMS engines. The most accessible variation was the GC, of course. Here a constant procession of 'Directors', Atlantics, 'Faringdons' and Robinson 2-8-0s was to be seen, and it was always intriguing to hear the Caprotti 'Faringdons', when working the 3.20pm Marylebone-Manchester, come bowling through Rugby at about 65, every beat separate and clearly audible. There was also a sprinkling of 'Sandringhams' and a few K3s on passenger work, and in 1936 the 'Football' series of B17s were allocated in fair numbers to the GC and displaced many of the native engines.

When this in turn proved unsatisfying, we would cycle the 15miles to Leamington on a Saturday afternoon, well packed up with sandwiches and a bottle of squash, to see the GWR. There was an undoubted attraction in the green livery and brass beadings, and the copper-capped chimneys, brass safety valve covers and impressive nameplates were worth something. But my main memories of those visits (apart from some saddle soreness) were audible: the staccato exhaust beats of 'Halls', 'Saints' and 'Castles' getting their trains on the move from the station stop, and the noise of the vacuum pumps, more forceful-sounding than the tinkle of those on the LNW engines, and the appalling burps of the large ejectors.

At this period my schooling was coming towards its end, and I determined to serve an engineering apprenticeship with the LMS. The choice lay between Crewe and Derby, and the natural first move was to visit the works at Crewe. They were turning out new 'Jubilees' at the time, and *Camperdown* and *Aboukir* were running-in from the North shed, a touch of colour in the gloomy station. The town, on a damp, murky afternoon in January 1936, gave me a feeling of utter revulsion. I reported to the offices at Chester Bridge clutching a letter agreeing to the visit, and was taken in tow by an elderly guide for the long trek through the many shops to the far west end of the 'new' erecting shop, something like 1½ miles each way as the crow flies. Tucked away in the paint shop was *J. B. Earle,* the last Leek & Manifold 2-6-4 tank, awaiting disposal instructions: alas, when they came they were to the knacker's yard. But undoubtedly what caused the biggest impression on me was the distance walked, much of it in a steady drizzle. No, I thought, Derby *must* be better than that.

I applied in writing to the Works Manager at Derby for an engineering apprenticeship, and got a very off-hand and discouraging reply: there were no vacancies, but if I cared to come for interview, they might bear me in mind for the future. I was all for abandoning the idea but my mother was wiser and recognised it for what it probably was, a test of resolve. So I was interviewed by the Assistant Works Manager, who was Mr E. S. Cox, though the occasion found no place in his book *Locomotive Panorama!* I can remember little of it myself, except for being shown a framed picture of a Midland 0-6-4 tank on the wall and being asked what sort of work it was used for and to name some visible parts. Anyway, it seemed to make a satisfactory impression, for on September 22, 1936 the heading 'POWELL, A. J., ENG. APPR., 10/- + 4/- WW.' and the clock number 2583 first appeared on a clock card. It continued to do so, with only changes in rate of pay at each birthday and a different clock number from time to time, until February 1941.

2/Derby Apprentice

Let me start by explaining, for the benefit of those of more tender years and brought up in terms of sandwich courses and sponsored degrees, that such systems were unknown on the LMS (and generally) in the 1930s. With a school leaving age of 14 from elementary schools and 16 from secondary and grammar schools, recruitment was into one of three streams, namely trade apprentices, engineering apprentices and pupils.

The trade apprentices thus did virtually a seven-year training until the age of 21, and their particular trade was chosen quite arbitrarily, either by themselves or by the staff people, at the outset. None of the present sophisticated system of 12months' basic training in a works training school and selection thereafter according to aptitude. However, they were encouraged to attend night school, and for those who made real progress there was the opportunity to switch to an engineering apprenticeship. On completion they were skilled fitters, erectors, moulders or what have you, but of course there was no guarantee of continued employment.

Engineering apprentices, by contrast, needed some School Certificate credits before being taken on at 16, and while working in just as practical a way with skilled tradesmen for four to five years, were given day release one day a week to study at the local Technical College, either for the National and Higher National Certificates or in some cases (including mine) for an external engineering degree. Two or sometimes three evenings of classes were also involved. Known in the shops as 'Privs', they were carefully programmed through a very wide cross-section of work, never more than three months on any section, by what was known as Progressive System of Workshop Training, under the eagle (but fairly benevolent) eye of Edgar Larkin, who finished his career in a very senior position with British Rail Engineering Ltd.

The number of pupils was very limited: they came generally at about 22, *after* getting a degree at university, and had a two-year condensed course after the style of the engineering apprentices, but without day release, on payment of a substantial premium.

Such was the system. I became a nominal part of it on the Monday morning, was sent off to get fixed up at the Technical College, and told to report to 9 Shop (the machine shop) the following morning at 7.55am, suitably overalled and ready for work. I was staying with relatives at Littleover, about 15min cycle ride away.

No.9 shop was presided over by a (to us) rather distant foreman, Frank May. His assistant made much more impression on us lads — George Wesley, who in later years took charge of the Erecting Shop. A man of medium height and fairly spare build, invariably in a blue serge suit and bowler hat, he would stalk into the shop five minutes after starting time with a determined look on his face and a darting eye. Woe betide the apprentice who was not on his feet looking active and with his machine running — even if it was not producing any work. His arrival thus tended to be heralded by a progressive squeal of driving belts as machines were started from the line shafting: individually motored machines were at that time in the minority.

My initiation was, like most before and many since, on 'Bottley's job'. This was an all-apprentice turning section, equipped mainly with about twenty old World War I 'Warner & Swazey' capstan lathes and doing straightforward steel turning and screwing work. Each was manned by a trade apprentice and, when available, one engineering apprentice. This motley crew were looked after, and hopefully kept in some sort of order, by a very short, rotund chargehand named Teddy Bottley, neat in brown warehouse coat and cloth cap. Teddy had a stand-up desk, open to the shop, at one end of the two lines of machines.

This long-suffering man would go toddling down the lines of lathes in pursuit of law and order, and reprimand offenders in a rather high-pitched voice. Contemporary with me was a Derby-bred engineering apprentice named Charlie Sharpe — he now works for Westinghouse — about 6ft 6in tall and given to draping himself over the lathe and discussing all and sundry, to the detriment of production. I can still see Teddy spotting Charlie in this posture and stumping along to him, steam nearly coming out of his ears. Looking up to him, he croaked 'I'll kick your bloody arse for you, Sharpe'. Alas, he would have needed to bring a soap box to stand on for the purpose!

Here, in common with the rest of the works, we worked a five-day week, from 7.55am to 5.30pm with an hour for lunch, making 42hr 55min. The rate of pay, 14/- a week, referred to a 47 hour week, including 7.55am to 12 noon on Saturdays, but recovery from the great depression was far from complete and it was not until the spring of 1939 that we reverted to the 47hr week. At age 16, therefore, for five days and with no production bonus, my take-home pay was 11/5d.

For me, the adjustment from a home/school environment to that of factory and lodgings was pretty traumatic. The weather was hot, there was an overall sickly stench of cutting oil, and though I was no prude I hated some of the trade apprentices for their crude language and equally crude interests. After ten days I was ready to pack up and go: fortunately I was talked out of it by wiser heads, and soon came to accept the atmosphere and camaradie and to revel in most of it.

The under-foreman who supervised Bottley's job and others was Harry Sharman, who had the (to me) unpleasant habit of chewing tobacco. He

14

would spend about ten minutes at a time at the gangway intersection near 'my' machine, watching points and chewing away, spitting at intervals with studied aim. When he had gone, there was a quite accurate circle marked out on the shop floor. 'Sharman was here' certainly preceded Kilroy!

From there my first move was to the brass turning section, and after a week on an antiquated 'wibbling' machine (milling hexagon flats on a variety of small fittings) — and on which the previously-mentioned Charlie Sharpe took the sleeve out of his boiler suit, along with some skin, when it caught on one of the cutters — was put on an almost brand-new Herbert 2S bar capstan lathe in the tender care of the setter-up, Charlie Hardy. This combination churned out vast numbers of pipe cones, setscrews and other small components from brass bar or tube, and within a month I was doing my own setting-up. Not only did I enjoy the work immensely, but I started getting bonus for it as well. My longest-lasting recollection of this work was of the 'Unbrako' screws in the toolholders which belied their name.

After three months surrounded by brass swarf and turnings, the brass fitting section welcomed me. The apprentices repaired tender water feed cocks, cylinder cocks, sand traps and ejectors, and other straight-forward components, while the tradesmen did the more demanding work on injectors, water gauge frames and the like. They had little time or (seemingly) inclination to guide or help us, and struck us as distinctly dour. In fact, one of them watched me all day on the first Monday grinding in some tender water feed cocks, which was quite a lengthy business — certainly the bonus seemed totally inadequate — without telling me what everybody else did: just assemble the cock with plenty of stiff grease on the plug surfaces, and it would pass the water test easily! From there it was the axlebox section, and then the motion benches.

Talking of the motion section, there was a series of heavy turnover fixtures for holding inside connecting rods while the big ends were being fitted. Now an inside connecting rod was no mean piece of steel, lifted by the mobile cranes and transported on tractor-hauled trailers. Imagine our amazement, then, when one day a labourer came marching down the shop with a connecting rod (admittedly without the big end strap and brasses) *on his shoulder!* Talk about Guinness for strength! Some champion weightlifter in training, perhaps? No, it was an experimental light alloy rod, one of a pair tried on, I think, a Class 3F shunting tank. How we cheered!

The last section in the machine shop on which I laboured, and that only briefly, was the one which assembled bogies and bissel trucks. Here I learned the hard way, and well, the skill of using a hammer and chisel, one which is forever retained once it has been acquired. The Stanier side-bolster trucks had two forked beams which transferred the pressure of the side control springs to the sliding bolster; these beams were oxy-coal gas cut from slab, in two planes, and it was necessary to put a large

15

radius (about ³⁄₈in, as I recollect) along two edges about a foot long. It would clearly have been straightforward to mill that radius on, and probably cheaper, too. However, I suppose that it was an apprentice hammer-and-chisel job deliberately, for training purposes — in which case it was sheer sadism. At the end of a week one's left hand had been hit so often instead of the head of the chisel that it was raw, bruised and ultra-tender — but, make no mistake, by that time you were wielding a hammer and chisel in tolerably expert fashion. It was too painful to do otherwise.

And nobody was allowed to hold the hammer shaft anywhere but at the end. Later, in the erecting shop, I saw one of the foremen go up to a youngster holding his hammer very near the head while doing some fairly light job. 'Let's have a look at that hammer of yours, lad'. He examined it with a very serious look. 'Hmm. Got a hacksaw?' There and then he put the hammer in a vice, sawed off all but about 4in of the shaft, gave it back to the amazed lad and said, 'You'll find that better for breaking toffee'.

A spell in the Central Materials Inspection Bureau followed. Here we draw-filed steel specimens for bend tests, assisted on the tensile machine, helped to do the crush tests on 6in concrete cubes from various construction jobs up and down the country — Lea Hall station, then being built, provided a lot, I recall — and listened to the Stores Department testing detonators on the sidings outside while the shunt engine was busy.

Wheel shop, boiler and fabrication shop, and boiler mounting shop all followed. In the former, we were involved in a variety of jobs, and the Assistant Foreman took a lot of personal interest in the apprentices' progress. We fitted the large rectangular keys after pressing wheels on the axles, always helped on the wheel balancing machine, and built up crank axles. All Stanier wheels had built-up balance weights which had a 95% lead, 5% antimony alloy poured in according to the out-of-balance shown up on the machine. Here, too, I had my first real acquaintance with electric welding: blowholes in new steel wheel castings revealed during machining were always having to be welded up, and I borrowed a welder's blue eyeshield glass to watch the process. Unfortunately, after the best part of a day of that, my face became two-tone — a normal pale-pink rectangular section round the eyes, and a rather angry red surround where the skin had been unprotected from the rays.

In the boiler mounting shop, the engineering apprentices were the 'inside' workers to a boilersmith and his mate, putting in all the internal copper steampipes, main steampipe and regulator head, working within the boiler barrel before it was tubed. The boilersmith that I worked for was a small swaggery individual named Alf Martin, an excellent tradesman who had worked on the Ljungstrom turbine locomotive during its trials on the Midland Division during 1927/8. If you suffered from claustrophobia, then God help you! You got in by the dome, of course, which was no problem for a normal lad, but by the time you came out finally, you had fitted the regulator head in the dome and coupled it up to the main steampipe, the joint not being accessible from the outside. That took up nearly half the space through which you had got in. You then had to climb out past the regulator head, standing on two planks across the bottom of the barrel to which you had already attached strong cord so that they could be subsequently retrieved. The G7 boilers for 0-6-0s and Class 2s were not too bad; the G9s for the Compounds were more difficult, because the Deeley regulator head was bigger; and the worst of all were the Lickey Banker (which I did on one occasion) and the Garratts, which were absolute swine!

During my spell there, one of the apprentices got stuck in a Garratt boiler and incurred an hour or more involuntary overtime having to take the regulator head out again before he could emerge. Needless to say, his mates made great play of packing up to go home at 5.30pm, having 'forgotten' that he was still incarcerated!

Then to the Erecting Shop (No 8) for about 18 months, and you were really amongst locomotives all the time. At that period Derby looked after all the Midland engines in England and their Fowler derivatives, together with the 2-6-4 and 2-6-2 tanks and Garratts. Some of the Stanier tanks were also in Derby's charge. A few other types came in from time to time, mainly for casual repairs or collision damage. Not necessarily in any particular order, the engineering apprentices worked on stripping, frames and horns, cylinder and valve liner reboring, pipework, cabs and tanks, motion erection and valve setting, and the like. Much of the work was fairly heavy — we were no strangers to 7lb hammers — and there were some curiously outdated practices still in use. For instance, an erector and I spent most of a day bedding the rear inside piston valve chest cover of a Compound on to the cylinder; we were not allowed to draw the studs from the face, and so we had to break up a square bastard file into lengths of about 2″ in order to be able to file the narrow face between them! And on the hard cylinder-quality iron, with a skin on it, that was not funny.

It would have been helpful if all entrants to the erecting shop could have started on the stripping section, because that was where you got the rough end of everyone's malpractices when the engine was last in works. It taught me, for instance, the value of a little oil when assembling things — fitters' best friend, I christened it — and of putting nuts on studs with a smear of graphite grease if they were going to work at boiler or cylinder heat: that way, the nut would come off the stud, years later, instead of pulling the stud out also.

Perhaps the best known character in No 8 shop in those days at the start of the war was 'Nigger' Wilson, a big, burly erector on the motion section, who had a stentorian voice and a wonderful flow of both wit and invective. Those apprentices who had not worked with him were, to say the least, awed, but those who had, and measured up to his requirements, held him in high regard. Towards the end of a tiring day, when you were beginning to flag, he would opine that what you needed was some haslet, guaranteed to put hair on your chest amongst other beneficial effects. If you believed 'Nigger', he had a plateful for his tea every evening, and it certainly seemed to sustain *him*!

Finally, after a spell in the iron foundry, coremaking, assisting in building up the moulds for cylinder castings (fascinating, this) and various straightforward floor- and box-moulding work, I spent the last four months of my apprenticeship over in 4 Shed, as Derby Motive Power Depot was known. (Nos 1, 2 and 3 sheds dated from the earliest Midland constituent days, were all roundhouses and within the confines of the locomotive works itself: No 1 was by now part of the Millwrights' shop, and used for crane repairs: No 2 was a store: and No 3 was in use as a shed for the smaller locomotives until just before World War II, when it was demolished).

If I learned nothing else in No 4 Shed, it taught me that conditions in a running shed in the winter were less than ideal. The work was filthy, the roof leaked, it was dark and one had to do much of the work by the smoky light of a duck lamp; an impenetrable yellow 'fog' of smoke crept through the place in the late afternoon when lighting-up of boilers started after examinations, and usually a howling, bitter wind blew through the place. Before plucking up courage to start work, and at intervals during the day, men would soak themselves in the warmth of a large cast-iron stove in one corner, always kept glowing dull red all over, and its long chimney kept clear by inserting the occasional detonator in the fire. They adopted a characteristic pose, facing outwards in a ring, legs apart at the 'stand easy', and hands spread out over their behinds, palms to the heat. Traces of smoke from scorching greasy overalls would rise in the gloom, and a voice laced with ecstasy would plead 'Move me, I'm burning!', the owner remaining rooted to the spot.

Nor was it merely the general environment in the shed that was poor; some of the jobs themselves had necessarily to be done under pretty grim conditions. One job we landed, for instance, was the removal of a set of superheater elements from (I think) a Class 5, due to the flues being blocked. About half the elements came out without too much difficulty, working in the smokebox on sacks laid in to inhibit the soot. A few more came out with the aid of a wire rope sling attached to the little pug, No 11217, standing on the turntable and pulling. But about half a dozen defied even this treatment — the downcomers pulled out straight without budging the part in the flues — and so yours truly was installed, crouched on top of the brick arch in the firebox, with a smoky duck lamp for illumination, and a longish dolly down the flue, belting them out with a 4lb lump hammer. Talk about the Black & White Minstrels; when you'd spent nearly a full day at that, you could say that you'd lived with one LM locomotive, anyway!

The high spot of the shed period, eagerly looked forward to, was the

18

day (more than one, if you could wangle it) when you went "Trent trials". Each engine fresh off the works, after a day on the steam pit alongside the shed having minor faults and leaks rectified, and after being weighed, went to Trent and back as a first run-in to check that things were right and bearings were running cool. This was my first experience of being on a moving steam locomotive on the main line, but it was really rather an anti-climax, for we jogged along at about 30mph with scarcely a breath of steam. There was absolutely no impression of the magic of a working steam locomotive.

As my 21st birthday approached, there were interviews with the Divisional Motive Power Superintendent and with Edgar Larkin. I opted to stay with the CM&EE Department, rightly or wrongly, because while the operation of motive power was a prime interest, the early stages of a Motive Power career sounded much less attractive than one in the works. Early in 1941, therefore, I set aside my overalls for a 9 to 5 job in the newly reorganised Production Office as a Technician, planning the production of a new batch of Class 5s and then 17 pounder anti-tank guns. Two years of that was followed, inevitably, by just over four years in the army. From the monsoon-lashed plains of Bengal I wrote to Edgar Larkin, by now Staff Assistant to the CME, asking about the chance of a job in the Locomotive Testing Station at Rugby (the building of which was about to be started) and, on return to England — to the snows of January 1947 — went for interview with him. As an alternative, I was offered a job as Mechanical Inspector at Derby Headquarters, concerned with the mechanical and operational performance of locomotives in traffic, in close collaboration with the Motive Power Department, the works and drawing office. Needless to say, I did not refuse. 'Living' could now develop with a vengeance.

3/The Mechanical Inspectors: The CME's Link with Motive Power

Wherever locomotive men foregather, it is a safe bet that, before long, the conversation will turn to ideas about how the locomotive fleet should be managed in service. The debate never seems to reach finality: men hold passionately to the opposite viewpoints of total control by the CME, providing power and men to meet the requirements of the operators, or of a dominant Operating role, with locomotives maintained in service to standards laid down by the CME and in the hands of drivers who are Operating staff in the same way as guards and shunters.

Convincing arguments can be advanced for and against each approach, and for intermediate ones: I do not propose to add to them here. Suffice it to say that, rightly or wrongly, on the LMS, and then on BR in steam days, the operation of the locomotive fleet came under the control of a Motive Power Superintendent (or similar title) who had a dual allegiance. He was responsible for the provision of power, in good order and suitably manned, at the right times to meet the Chief Operating Superintendent's specification (ie the timetable), and he controlled the locomotive fleet and the depots and signing-on points accordingly. He had to maintain the locomotives between visits to the works, to the standards agreed with the Chief Mechanical Engineer.

Now Chief Mechanical Engineers were, basically, managers for the works maintenance of the locomotive, carriage and wagon fleets. Design activities and new construction were seldom more than about 10% of their workload. But what happened in service quickly impacted on the maintaining works: the 'under and awaiting repair' percentage has always been subjected to the most critical scrutiny — and not only within the CME's own organisation — and repair costs needed to be budgeted for each year. If these indices were to be kept within bounds or improved, there was need for good feedback of reliable information which could be used for 'refining the breed'.

The Motive Power Superintendent had a number of people involved in such feedback, both at headquarters at Euston and in each of the (old) Divisions, who attended the more important, or unusual, mechanical casualties and devoted much time to repair practices and histories at sheds. Much valuable information flowed to the CME from this source, particularly in alerting him quickly to unexpected problems as they became apparent, and highlighting areas which needed campaign investigation. They also reported on specific items at the request of the CME, including new fittings (self-cleaning smokeboxes were an example amongst many) provided for the benefit of the Motive Power staff.

But the progressive refinement of a fleet of nearly 8,000 locomotives is an avaricious consumer of information and distilled experience, and some fields could only be adequately explored if lengthy, full-time investigations, cutting across Divisional boundaries, could be made. This tended to conflict with the concept of keeping the railway running day-to-day, which inevitably governed the working of the Motive Power Department people. So the CME felt a real need for a small team of technically qualified Mechanical Inspectors, answerable to his Chief Technical Assistant, who could be deployed as his eyes and ears, on the footplate, in the works and in sheds, to take firm hold on problems and worry them to a solution, involving the Drawing Office as necessary. At headquarters at Derby he had four or five of them under a Senior Mechanical Inspector. This was the team I was privileged to join, early in 1947.

At that time the senior man was Derek Ritson: on his early and untimely death Jack Smith took over, and with him were George Fisher, John Lawson, Norman Lloyd and myself. In addition, later on Ian Hunter came in on the edge of the team: though nominally a development draughtsman, the distinction from the mechanical inspectors became somewhat blurred in his case. We occupied part of a large, high and rather gloomy room on the ground floor at Nelson Street (we moved upstairs the following year) but it was unusual if any more than two of the desks were occupied during the day — and that was as it should be.

The two junior inspectors normally took all the casualty work in collaboration with the Divisional Motive Power Inspectors; the Midland Divisional man at Derby was Bill Thorley, who retired in 1972 as Senior Traction Officer at Board HQ. George Fisher, an ex-Motive Power man of great practical experience, was particularly concerned with the then new Class 2 and Class 4 2-6-0s, the Caprotti valve gear on the Class 5s, and the five Reidinger-valve gear 2-6-0s. On the poppet valve gears John Lawson was something of a specialist, too, following up many of the shed examinations and modifications in conjunction with the manufacturers.

Of course, it never divided quite as neatly as that, and in time each one of us got our own spheres of influence, while having a sufficient knowledge of what the others were doing, by round table discussion, that we could step into any breech as necessary. To illustrate the range we covered, some of my specialities were refractory concrete 'brick' arches, the rough riding of the rebuilt 'Royal Scots' (of which more in a later chapter), variations in valve setting to prevent axlebox knock (also to be dealt with later), the design of a safer type of water gauge protector, and the cylinder lubrication problems which arose with the early BR standard locomotives.

At that time I was averaging 10,000 miles a year or more on the footplate, riding supernumary (of course) to the normal crew. One had to be relatively unobtrusive (if anyone 6ft 1½in and 13stone can be!), interfering not at all — because we had no Motive Power Inspector status — observing everything, commenting or answering questions tactfully, helping out in various ways in cases of difficulty, and often recording in some detail. We were on first-name terms with virtually all the shed Mechanical Foremen and many of the District Locomotive Superintendents and their Assistants. Standard equipment in bulging briefcases was a notebook, overalls, scarf and dirty cap, torch, special soap for grimy hands and towel, and sponge cloths, supplemented according to the occasion by long feeler gauges, or drawings, or a brown paper parcel of urgently needed spare parts.

And what did we achieve? It must be said right at the start that results were often slow to come to fruition. Sometimes problems could be overcome by minor changes in, say, works repair practice; but many needed design modifications which, by the time the requirement and nature of the problem were identified, design work done, the approach cleared with the Motive Power Superintendent, an experiment mounted to prove the validity of the modification, experience gained and in due course financial authority obtained for universal application, spread over several years. Some never did get put right. Take the case, for instance, of the leakage from top feed clack box joints on the Stanier engines. Within the constraints of the existing oval man-hole cover on which the clack boxes were fitted, all sorts of alternative jointing materials, face-to-face joints, clips on the delivery pipes and the like were tried and found wanting or were rejected on grounds of cost; meantime the tell-tale rust marks and lime stains on the boiler clothing continued. Thank heaven that the BR standard boilers were fitted with the Southern's clack box which eliminated this trouble 'at a stroke'.

But there were real benefits to show for our efforts. The technique of applying manganese steel liners to axleboxes and guides, for instance, developed from our work with the experimentally-fitted locomotives to the point where the wholesale fitting to earlier Class 5s could be justified by the elimination of one of the two intermediate repairs normally carried out between general overhauls at 200,000 — 250,000 miles. The spring link problem and weight adjustment technique using a range of load-bearing cotters in fixed links was fathered through the development stage by the mechanical inspectors. So was the redesign of the inside big end brasses of the big passenger engines after the disastrous early post-war years. Just three examples out of many.

From the personal point of view, of course, it gave me a unique opportunity to know, from first-hand experience, just what really went on, both on the footplate and in the motive power depots, in everyday life. As in so many fields, one came across the good and the not-so-good; depots where management was keen, maintenance conscientious, locomotives kept reasonably clean, and the footplate staff responded with a high standard of performance to match. At Rugby, for instance, it was a joy to study the 'X-day' examination cards: clearly the examining fitter went over the engine with something like a fine toothcomb, and the recorded repairs were overwhelmingly the little things — the odd loose bolt, a split pin badly fitted, a minor leak — which, if neglected, became big things, weeks later.

There were the other sort, too — bad facilities, skimped repairs, dirt everywhere. Kingmoor was undoubtedly one of these latter: when we had four Class 5s transferred from there to Newton Heath in 1957, the preliminary examination for necessary repairs there filled a couple of big 'X' cards on both sides for each engine! Oh, yes, you could get a fair idea of depot standards and morale by looking through repair cards and not surprisingly, drivers and firemen tended to respond in kind.

The steam locomotive, rugged, sometimes crude, able to tolerate a fair measure of abuse, depended on a triangular partnership of driver, fireman and maintaining and servicing staff. And when the chips were down, at the depot where the fitters were up to their elbows in muck, the ashpits overflowed, and any old wagon of coal went up the coaling plant for any engine that came next, that was when locomotive breeding became apparent. And that was what the mechanical inspectors were concerned with.

4/The Fowler Legacy

The Midland Railway bequeathed the LMS Railway some 2,948 locomotives. Under the Anderson regime after grouping, and with Fowler's acquiescence, Midland practice continued: some 1,400 further locomotives of basically Midland type were produced for the LMS up to 1932, or acquired from the Somerset & Dorset, alongside more advanced classes such as the 'Royal Scots', the Horwich 2-6-0s and the 2-6-4 tanks. Indeed, 45 Class 4F 0-6-0s were built as late as 1937-1941. So on the formation of BR in 1948, the LMS in its turn handed over some 2,608 locomotives of a generic Midland type.

Now the Midland Railway had been a fairly prosperous organisation, and could well afford to pamper its locomotive fleet. There were even suggestions of a Society for the Prevention of Cruelty to Midland Engines. The fleet was not driven hard, nor intensively used, and its maintenance was of a high order — labour-intensive, for many of the facilities provided at depots were pretty rudimentary, but devoted — and under these conditions it had a long life, often with rebuilding at an intermediate stage. But there was little pressure for further development or refining.

As soon as the conditions under which the Midland locomotives had prospered changed in the inter-war years, and particularly in the depression years of the 1930s, the Midland fleet started to look very jaded. Common user working, accelerations and demotion to second-grade services, and all the economies involved in keeping heads above water in a cruel national economic climate quickly revealed their inherent weaknesses. And they were many.

Let us start at the frames. By the standards of the time they were fairly robust, though the Midland refusal to use the horse-shoe hornblock rather than separate axlebox guides left them rather prone to cracking at the top corners of the horns. Being invariably inside-cylinder, and everything behind the driving axle being occupied by firebox, there was nothing that could be done to stiffen up the frames against racking stresses. The horn clips, usually studded on to the bottom of the axlebox guides, could not be kept tight for long because of the frame flexing. Another oddity was that because of limitations in the length of frame plate that Derby could machine, almost all the 4-4-0s had to have frame plates in two pieces, lapped behind the bogie at the inside motion plate.

But the most curious feature was the front buffer beam attachment on the 0-6-0s and others. To allow unrestricted access to the front cylinder covers and pistons, the buffer beam was bolted on. And to prevent minor collisions bending the main frames, the buffer beam itself was riveted to two horizontal channels which in turn were bolted to gusset angles on the frames. These channels and their bolted attachment took all the buffing and drawgear loading, and due to their rather flimsy dimensions were perpetually bent and loose. Other railways could rivet buffer beams direct to the gussets and still manage to withdraw pistons: not the Midland.

Then the axleboxes: they were really rather prehistoric. They consisted of a steel horse-shoe body, with parallel sides and square crown into which fitted (loose) the 'brass'. This located by a circular machined boss which engaged in a matching recess in the crown of the steel body. A straightforward keep containing an oil pad, held in place by the pin of the spring D-link, completed the assembly. You could only get at the pad by dropping the wheels, of course! Lubrication, from oil box or mechanical lubricator, was taken to the crown of the steel box and thence to the top boss of the brass and the crown of the bearing. The bearing area was very inadequate — the use of inside crank axles with two pairs of eccentric sheaves leaves no room for journals more than about 8½in long — and so hot boxes were all too frequent. These occurred because of various deficiencies in the oil supply, inadequately backed up by the underpad, and also due to the fore-and-aft 'roll' which developed on the bearing when, for instance, Class 4Fs were involved in heavy, slow-speed pulling; all these could prevent the maintenance of a proper oil film.

The Midland's ideas on springing were rudimentary in the extreme. No such things as J-hangers on the frames with adjustable spring links in tension as most lines used, but just crude, non-adjustable links in compression, an inherently unstable arrangement dependent on the integrity of the spring buckle securing device. So if, when you weighed the locomotive or tender, some adjustment of axle weights was required, there was no alternative but to take down the links and 'jump' or 'draw' them in the smithy. Mind you, they could not even weigh a locomotive in Derby Works — the Motive Power Department had the only axle weigh-bridges on the Midland Division, one at Derby, and engines ex-works had to be put over that. (The compounds had coil springs on the driving axle, and bounced their way around in sometimes lively fashion).

The cylinders and motion on Midland engines were pretty appalling, and in some respects the later piston-valve engines were worse than the ones with slide valves. Only on the 990s was any attempt made to design a cylinder casting to allow steam to get in and out of the cylinders easily. These were the only ones with nice straight ports, and with outside admission the exhaust must have been pretty free, despite the 1⅛in lap and limited travel. All the other piston valve engines had very crooked and restricted ports, the valves were undersized for the size of cylinder, and the port openings typical of short-travel valves. And to cap it all, on the Class 2Ps and Belpaires they then put these wretched valves *below* the cylinders, so that live and exhaust steam had to fight their way between the two cylinder barrels (20½in on the Midland engines) in more constricted passages. Hence the Derby 'roar' instead of anything resembling clean, sharp and separate exhaust beats.

Mind you, the absolute horror in the cylinder field was No 2290, the Lickey banker. Four cylinders, only two piston valves with crossed ports to the adjacent cylinder, and abysmally short lap and travel. No wonder the Bromsgrove men preferred 0-6-0 tanks — they would at least *go*. The cylinders of the banker have, I believe, been preserved — as an awful warning to others, I imagine.

One feature was good, however, and that was the mounting of the return crank on the driving crankpin. Stanier recognised its worth and perpetuated it in preference to the usual square attachment. The crank was held by four studs in the end of the crankpin, the nuts of which tightened on to copper washers, alignment being maintained by a 'key' integral with the return crank which registered in a keyway across the end of the pin. Once fitted, it was there, firm as a rock, until you wanted it off again.

The boilers in themselves were not bad, despite the use of a single set of flanged plates and standard tube layout for all fireboxes between 7ft and 9ft long. The ratio of free gas area to grate area suffered with the bigger grates, but surprisingly it seemed to make little difference at any normal steaming rates. The Belpaire fireboxes were straight, slab-sided affairs, but at the relatively low working pressures were not particularly troublesome for the boilersmiths. The flat-bottomed smoke-boxes were not always easy to keep airtight, however. The front tubeplate was riveted on to an angle on the end of the barrel, with rivets in tension, which was less desirable than a circular drum-head tubeplate set into the barrel, but apart from the need for some recaulking at the seam it appeared reasonably satisfactory.

What was bad was the sheaf of internal pipes referred to in Chapter 2. There was no steam manifold on the firebox, as most railways used. Instead, internal copper pipes ran from the dome to facings on the backplate for the two injector steam valves, the small ejector steam valve, and the blower/sanding valve, and to a facing near the front of the boiler barrel for the large ejector steam valve. From the backplate, internal pipes also ran from the two clackboxes to delivery points near the front tubeplate, and from the blower valve to a connection on the front tubeplate by the superheater header. All these pipes threaded their way between the firebox crown stays in a rather haphazard manner, and for those carrying steam any chafing leading to ingress of water brought major problems, usually involving special shopping of the locomotive and removal of a block of tubes in order to get access. Certain Midland

26

standard boiler fittings were poor in the extreme. Perhaps the most important were the live steam injectors, which were perpetuated on all new construction until after World War II. They were frequently temperamental starters, and had little range of delivery: there was usually only one position of the water handle where they would work at all cleanly. The vacuum ejectors were not very efficient, particularly if boiler pressure was at all down. The steam sanding valve was combined with the blower valve in a body always placed just above the firehole, out of reach of the driver. If there was a blowback, the blower was virtually inaccessible to anyone! And the combined vacuum/steam brake valve! It was supposed to give a graduated steam brake application on engine and tender matching the reduction of vacuum in the trainpipe, but in practice was one of those all-or-nothing affairs. To operate the steam brake on the engine when running light, without vacuum, you had to hook the linkage back manually for release of the brake. So everyone used vacuum, although there was no vacuum brake as such on the engine or tender.

Nor must we forget other aspects of the driver's environment. On the passenger engines, the reversing screw had to be perched on top of the rear wheel splasher inside the fairly narrow cab. That left nowhere for the driver to sit, except on top of the reversing screw — on a wooden board, with a slot down the middle through which the cutoff indicator (equally spaced 'notches' with no percentage markings) was visible. I've heard of 'driving by the seat of the pants', but that was ridiculous! Then, except on the Compounds and some of the LMS-built locomotives, a plain regulator handle in the top quadrant meant that the driver had to stand up to open or close it. Hence the proliferation of front cab windows; imagine shunting a yard on that basis, standing up looking over or round the firebox to catch a glimpse of the shunter's hand signal! There were drivers who carried round a home-made attachment which they fitted to the regulator handle with wing nuts so that they could operate the regulator and look out of the cab side at the same time.* Oh, yes, and the whistle handle was also central above the firebox, so you had to stand to operate *that*, also.

So let nobody suppose that Midland engines were fun for the driver, quite apart from the indifferent protection that the cab offered. On the Class 4Fs, when running with the damper open (there was only one, at the front) a fine stream of ash from the ashpan was driven by the air flow to come up through various gaps, holes and slots into the cab at the back of the firebox. That made things even better!

But the inbuilt weaknesses of design, notably in the frames and axleboxes, meant that 50,000 miles between intermediate works repair was very good going — 40,000 was more typical of many of them — and they could be pretty rough by then. A run-down Compound on an

*See *The Locomotive*, November 15 1930, page 391.

express coming down the curves of the Peak Forest line from Millers Dale to Rowsley was an experience that you did not necessarily want to repeat!

Some steps were taken to try to improve the hot box record, but they achieved little because the journal sizes could not be changed. There was some changeover to cast manganese bronze boxes, using dovetailed gunmetal inserts and poured whitemetal between them. But not only did these inserts loosen under the pounding meted out to them in service, thus leading to the breakup of the whitemetal, but from time to time part or the whole of one leg of an axlebox would break off, either through a spring link hole or at a section weakened by a dovetail slot. Then some axleboxes of the Stanier type, in cast steel with a pressed-in brass, were fitted, notably to the Class 4Fs, and while mechanically satisfactory did nothing to overcome the problem of journal size.

The 4Fs — everyone at Derby knew them as the 'Big Goods'! — had another endearing habit, that of snapping off outside crankpins, usually the driving ones. The coupling rod journals were, if I remember rightly, no more than 3¾ in diameter, and if the engine got into anything of a slip when pulling hard and then one pair of wheels got a grip to stop it, off would come a crankpin like a crisp carrot, more or less flush with the wheel boss, and showing a sizeable fatigue flaw. The answer was plain to see — bigger pins. But that would have required new coupling rods, and the cure would probably have been more costly than the disease.

The frames, cylinders and brakes of the Compounds were a positive dog's breakfast. Each frame plate was in *three* pieces: a rear section to the usual motion plate position, then a middle section forked at the front end to accept the three cylinders as a unit, and finally a front section similarly forked at the rear end to lap with the middle section and the cylinder flanges. The front section was shallow and weak, and invariably crumpled, together with the gussets, at the least impact — they were nearly as much in the furnace for straightening as they were in service. A deeper profile was later adopted, and this made some improvement.

The cylinders were pretty dreadful — small wonder that the thermal efficiency of the Compounds was no better than that of a modern simple. There was a piston valve below and for the HP cylinder, short on travel and badly ported, and vertical slide valves for the two LP cylinders. The lubrication of the slide valves was never very satisfactory, despite trials with atomisation of the oil, even though the steam temperatures which they endured were low, and this led to very heavy scoring of the valve faces. In addition, the cylinders themselves were rather prone to fractures. So after World War II a decision was taken to change over to cast steel cylinders with cast iron liners, and the steel foundry at Crewe, whose products at that time were not notable for quality or homogeneity, had the time of their lives. It would be an understatement to say that this change was not a success: the internal ports and passages were so tortuous that it was extremely difficult to clear reliably the core sand from them and fettle them effectively. As a result the scoring of the LP valve faces got steadily worse, to the point where engines were being shopped at 20,000 miles, and in some cases much less, for remachining of the port faces.

But the steam brakes on the Compounds were quite notorious. On each side a steam brake cylinder was suspended between the coupled wheel brake hangers, with an uncompensated clasp arrangement of rigging, and a metal hose steam connection which was *most* unreliable. Drivers had to watch the brake like a hawk when working light engine, getting it well warmed up before needing to use it, and even then it was as weak as dishwater. And during the war they tried to use them on unfitted freight trains!

With the LMS versions of the Midland designs, there was some 'cosmetic' treatment of chimneys and domes, and improved tenders, but that was just about all. A half-hearted attempt was made to improve the front end of the Class 2Ps, but it did not lead to much. The cylinders were reduced in diameter and the boiler pressure increased to compensate, but the cylinder layout remained just as poor. Double-headed piston valves were applied in an attempt to get the steam through better, and they were marginally better in this respect, but the valves were much more difficult to fit, and even worse to get out, for they suffered severely from carbon build-up.

Apart from the Midland designs, the Fowler regime saw a number of new designs produced, some of which marked important steps forward. There were the Horwich 2-6-0s, 'Royal Scots' and 'Baby Scots', the 2-6-4 and 2-6-2 tanks, the Class 7F 0-8-0s and the Garratts. Design thinking on these classes was curiously mixed. Axleboxes were fairly generously proportioned except on the 2-6-2 tanks, the Class 7Fs and the Garratts, where the disastrous 'Big Goods' proportions were adopted, the cylinder design was fair on all of them — not in the Stanier class for steam flow, but reasonable — but the 2-6-2 tanks and Garratts had poor, short-travel valve gear and were sluggish, whereas the others had fairly long-travel valves and were very sprightly in performance. But many of the weaknesses of the Midland designs — the frames, the manganese bronze axleboxes, the spring gear, and the standard fittings — carried through into these designs of the 1920s, and were not really dispelled until the advent of the Stanier influence, if at all.

To sum up, therefore, the Fowler years saw the first moves to break away from long outdated Midland practices — with many a longing, backward glance meantime — but really did very little in total to bring the LMS locomotive fleet up to a form that would match the conditions of the 1930s and later. That role fell to William Stanier.

5/The Stanier Influence and Beyond

The Great Western Railway was one whose locomotive practice never gained my wholehearted approval (although they managed fairly well without it!). Nevertheless, one was forced to admit that there were features of their design practice which were quite elegant, and the standard of finish was good: one thinks of brake rigging and the wire-wound handles of some steam valves as examples of this refinement. So it was perhaps natural that William Stanier, when he moved from Swindon to the LMS in 1932, should look critically at what he found there and draw on his previous experience to institute changes — and mostly changes very much for the better, These changes generally went right through every design produced under his direction in a consistent manner.

There were, of course, mistakes. The initial adoption of relatively low superheat was undoubtedly one, and it can be argued that the use of a regulator in the superheater header — though fine in principle — and the reversion to dry sanding were others. Stanier was, however, big enough in stature to recognise that the LMS was a different organisation from that he had left, and geared to work in somewhat different ways, and that required a change in course, But any mistakes were totally overshadowed by the benefits derived from other new features which came with him.

From the point of view of maintenance within the Motive Power Department, undoubtedly the biggest boon was the virtual elimination of hot axleboxes and big ends. The coupled wheel journals on his engines were of generous size (those on the Class 5s, for instance, were 8½ diameter by 11in long); the axleboxes were of cast steel with a horse-shoe shaped brass pressed in, and carrying a thin, continuous whitemetal bearing surface. The high pressure area of the crown was uninterrupted by oil grooves — the mechanical lubricator feed was channelled to distributing grooves on the horizontal centre line of the journal, to be taken into the bearing area by wedge action. The under-keep, which could be slid out (except on crank axles, of course) for pad examination and drainage of water, was generous and the underpad itself was carefully designed. Tender boxes, too, were of good size with good interior accessibility. So the Stanier engines soon established an enviable record. In 1939, for example, there were only 75 hot coupled axleboxes on the 1,000 two-cylinder taper boiler engines in service: for the best five classes totalling 810 engines the figure was 47, or one hot box per engine every 16 years 8 months. The Class 8F 2-8-0s suffered not a single hot coupled box during 1939.

The other big area of advantage was in the boiler and smokebox. With the tapered boiler barrel, Stanier brought the Swindon ideas on the geometry of the Belpaire firebox: no longer a collection of flat surfaces on the wrapper, but a series of continuous curves. These may have caused some heart-searching in the boiler shop at Crewe when being built, but there was an immense payoff in freedom from stay breakage and similar troubles, and in copper firebox life. Many Stanier boilers built in the 1930s were cut up at the end of steam with the original copper fireboxes, apart from the tubeplates. And the circular smokebox, sitting secure on a proper saddle, needed no action to keep it airtight, nor did the smokebox door with its conical metal-to-metal seating and centre dart fastening — another direct Swindon import — provided the seating was brushed clear of char.

Furthermore, they were all drivers' engines, in that they would perform well on a light rein, but equally they could be hammered and thrive on it. The front ends were magnificent: large straight-ported piston valves, ample steam pipes and gently-curved, tapering exhaust passages in the saddle brought together in a short, straight blast-pipe gave a very easy steam circuit, from superheater to chimney. You only had to listen to a nicely warmed-up Class 5 when opened out to know that there were no bottlenecks there.

Talking of drivers, it is rather amazing how long it took for the characteristics of a slide valve regulator with first and main valves to be understood, not only by outside observers but also by some testing staff. The drivers understood it, of course, and could be regularly observed, after a period of full regulator working, to close the regulator completely and reopen it to the desired degree for easier working. In the Stanier version, horizontally in the dome, the first valve gave a port opening of about one-eighth of the total area through the full-open regulator. That was sufficient at normal rates of working to give a steam chest pressure about 100lb/sq in below boiler pressure. Thereafter the port opening increased progressively as the handle was raised, up to the maximum. But when the regulator was closed from the full-open position, the main valve stayed fully open for about a third of the quadrant, closing uniformly from there. Thus, if the handle was in the mid-position, it could mean that the regulator was open little more than the first valve, or was nearly fully open: it all depended how it had got there. Fig 1 shows these characteristics.

On the tender engines, the cab and high-sided tender combination gave very good weather protection for the crew, and reasonable freedom from draughts. There have been derogatory remarks in the past in the technical press about the standard wooden tip-up seats, but I found them surprisingly comfortable. They could be instantly put up out of the

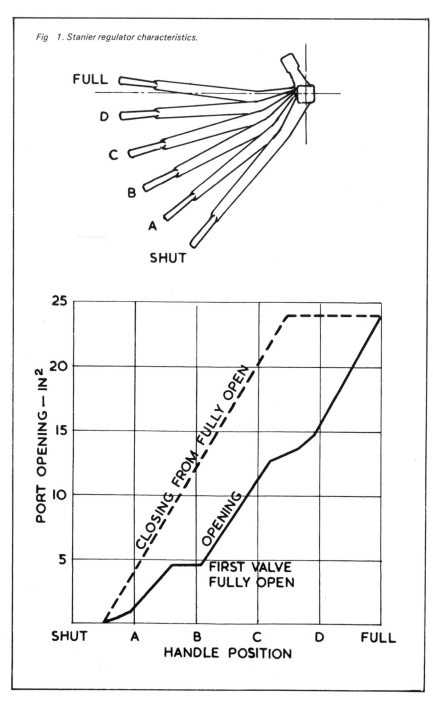

Fig 1. Stanier regulator characteristics.

FULL

D

C

B

A

SHUT

PORT OPENING — IN²

25

20

15

10

5

CLOSING FROM FULLY OPEN

OPENING

FIRST VALVE
FULLY OPEN

SHUT   A   B   C   D   FULL
HANDLE POSITION

way, and they withstood the hard usage from fitters' tools and hob-nailed boots far better than the much-vaunted upholstered bucket seats on the LNER Pacifics and others. And there were a surprising number of drivers who did not like to sit down when they were running.

With the exception of the blower valve, which remained the Midland-type valve placed above the firehole door, all the fittings the driver needed were within convenient reach from the sitting position.

The bunkers of the 4,000gallon tenders were designed to be self-trimming and in this they were reasonably successful. It is not easy, of course, to make them so under the varieties of coal which might be loaded: the great slabs of hard Yorkshire that were the norm at Camden, which formed a constant challenge for the coal pick, or the smaller lump and cobbles common in Scotland, or some of the ghastly mixtures of dross and ovoids that were sometimes the lot of freight depots. So after three or four tons had been burnt, some coals tended to hang back a bit and needed raking forward or a long reach with the shovel, while others were for ever inundating the footplate from under the doors. There was built-in provision for spraying the coal on the later tenders to keep the dust down. The tender footplate layout was very neat and spacious, thanks to the mounting of the water scoop and hand brake handles on the front bulkhead with bevel drive downwards to the shafts.

From the riding point of view, the Stanier engines were generally very smooth, and the Pacifics and 2-6-4 tanks particularly so. Side-bolster bogies and bissel trucks were standard (although the little Ivatt Class 2 engines marked the first departure from this): the side bolsters, set at something like 5ft centres — inevitably less on bissel trucks—transferred the weight to the bogie via large circular friction pads, giving a steady engine which was relatively immune to rolling or nosing. Because of the spherical surfaces on the bolster cups—or 'spittoons'—and the use of equalising beams, the bogie frames themselves were virtually relieved of load-carrying. They were primarily there to keep axles in line and transfer the side thrust. You could insert a pinchbar under the front stay and over the axle and rock the bogie frames up and down easily while the bogie was carrying its rated 20tons or more. So the sort of accident that befell No 60700 at Peterborough in 1955, when the bogie frame fractured and derailed engine and train, could not happen. By the same token, I think that the derailment of No 46207 on straight plain line at Weedon in 1951, allegedly due to the tight fitting of a bogie axlebox in the guides, must have required a coincidence with other faults which were not brought to light.

Now, from all this nobody should get the idea that the Stanier engines were perfect; they had their weaknesses like most others, even if they were fewer than on most. Take spring gear and axleboxes as an example (for they are nearly inseparable). Good as the axleboxes were on the journals, the whitemetal faces to the axlebox guides permitted the development of a fair amount of knock — .060in was quite common at shopping — and this did not do the springs any good, poised unstably as they were on compression spring links. So, in the Fairburn/Ivatt era, the use of manganese steel liners on boxes and guides was perfected, and the changeover made to tension links with 'mutton-chop' brackets, the links being first screwed and subsequently solid with weight-adjusting cotters. This killed axlebox knock largely, and benefited spring life (and the life of coupling rod joint pins also).

Along with these development went the universal adoption of full horse-shoe horn blocks (except on trailing coupled wheels under narrow fireboxes) and the simple, and very effective, 'Horwich' hornstay bolted to shorted extension 'legs' of the frame plate. These kept very tight.

Two other features are perhaps worth mentioning. The first — not confined to the LMS, for the LNER used them for a fairly long period also — was needle roller bearings for the generality of valve gear pins. These were widely used on the pre-war Stanier engines, but supply problems killed them off during the war and they were not reverted to afterwards. They were found to offer little improvement in wear as compared with bronze bushes, they were sensitive to breakdown, or missing, of the grease lubrication, and where the angular movement was small (as for instance with the crosshead arm pin) they could cause uneven wear and 'brinelling' of the pin.

The other item was grease lubrication, which came in extensively in the 1930s for motion pins, brake and spring gear, and the like. It gradually made headway, depending on the integrity of the greasing done at depots, which in turn partly depended on their having satisfactory greasing equipment. It was also affected by experimental work to find the most suitable grease — and we tried a few that were far from suitable. I think it fair to say that we never *did* get a robust and reliable portable greasing device: perhaps nothing but a static high-pressure plant would do the job. Problems arose with grease distribution round brake and spring gear pins where the rotation was negligeable. And if a pin was missed at one or two fortnightly greasings, the grease holes and channels became blocked with hardened grease which no portable 'gun' would push through. At least on the motion pins the driver applied oil (certainly) in addition to the fitter's mate applying grease (hopefully) and the resulting lubrication was sufficient. The battle continued long after I opted out!

On post-war engines, too, the top-feed leakage problem was fairly sucessfully tackled, using a new cover casting with the clackboxes integral with it. After some initial problems with the clacks themselves — of which more in Chapter 11 — the whole arrangement settled down well. At the same time, the smaller engines were fitted with the excellent 'Monitor' live-steam injectors, thus escaping from the slavery of the Midland design.

Other refinements were also brought in. There was a new, light, bar-framed bissel truck which proved very satisfactory (and it did not have those forked beams which I referred to so painfully in Chapter 2!). New-type cylinder drain cocks with vertical poppet valves and simpler operating linkage — at least that was the intention — made their appearance too, though they seemed rather susceptible to trapping any pieces of broken valve ring that came their way, causing a blow and straining the operating gear. In passing, one may mention that the piston valve rings used on LM locomotives — six on all long travel valve heads — were not particularly robust, being only $\frac{1}{4}$in wide, and it was by no means unknown for them to be broken during valve insertion, let alone by wear. If this were not realised at the time, and the broken ring trapped in the port, the result was often a bent combination lever as soon as the engine was moved. The problem was very much eased by the post-war adoption of differential valve heads. The rear head was made $\frac{1}{8}$in smaller in diameter than the front one, the liners being bored to match, thus allowing the back head to pass through the front liner more easily without disturbing the rings or the brass ring stops.

And just to show that it is rare to get anything for nothing, there was the adoption of external tender water sieves. The normal ones in the tender tank were a nuisance during the autumn leaf season in particular, when any blockage of the sieves meant emptying the tank to clear them. So the later tenders had an external sieve box with a vertical perforated plate: the water could be shut off and the plate dropped out and cleared very conveniently. Fine, you may say. Yes, but in frosty weather there was freezing trouble with this exposed box, and not only were frost fires provided at water columns, but we even had to provide them alongside tenders on depots to stop the sieve boxes freezing up.

For never let it be forgotten that the steam locomotive lived, and got by, in a hard world. Even where the upper works were made to shine (which was not by any means universal!) the part below the footframing was usually immersed in varying degrees of muck. The depots which prepared it, put it away after work and maintained it were, generally, pretty crude places, and the work involved was rough — as anyone who has ever watched a fire and ashpan being cleaned after a main-line run would testify. The maintenance staff concerned were no less skilled than, say, their works counterparts, but they were working, often in the open, frequently in near-darkness and usually against an operating deadline. Perhaps the mark of Stanier's greatness, which was further built upon by his successor CMEs, was that he produced a fleet of locomotives which would perform entirely creditably, even brilliantly, when subjected to such condition. Furthermore, the standards achieved by Ivatt and based on the Stanier marque, were not surpassed, seldom reached even, elsewhere — and I do not exclude the BR standard locomotives from this evaluation

6/ The Class 5 — The Engineman's Friend

It would be quite superfluous for me to devote space to the building history, dimensions and variants of the famous 'Black Fives'. Anyone seeking such details is referred to other books on the subject.* Suffice it to say that these locomotives constituted the largest single class — 842 in number — on BR. They were found throughout the land, from Bournemouth and Swansea to Stranraer and Thurso.

It hardly needs to be said that they were held in the highest esteem by all enginemen, and with every justification. A simple machine to drive, not sensitive to individual enginemen's techniques, however bizarre, easy to fire and quite effective in steaming with a thick or thin one, immune to fire-throwing unless grievously mishandled, steady on their feet, and comfortable to ride on — could a man want more? There was no climbing about inside the frames to do any oiling, and they seemed fully at home on any kind of work, uninhibited by route restrictions except on the more obscure branches. Small wonder that enginemen perked up when they knew they had one to work, and almost saw haloes round their chimneys.

My first real contact with the Class 5s came when they were still fairly new. Armstrong-Whitworth were rapidly turning out the Nos 5225-5451 order, and quite a number were allocated to the Midland Division, undertaking a lot of the fastest trains even under the 1938 accelerations. Prior to that, however, one of their regular workings was the 4.30pm Manchester Central to St. Pancras, due out of Derby at 6.4. I used this train every Friday night as far as Leicester on my way home: it was allowed 38min from Derby, with a 2min stop at Loughborough. For 29.3miles that timing may not sound very impressive, but the snag was that the seven or eight-coach train that rolled into Derby was there reinforced by another three coaches and four or five — even six on occasion — loaded 3,000gallon milk tanks from the Derbyshire and Staffordshire creameries. So south of Derby the Class 5 had a gross load usually in excess of 450 tons on her tail, and that was no easy task.

With a faintly downhill run to Trent Junction, we would be doing the best part of 70 before shutting off for the curve. But from the

*The Stanier Black Fives, by J. F. Clay. (Ian Allan, 1972).
Stanier Locomotives, by Brian Haresnape. (Ian Allan, 1970).

Loughborough restart, on that gentle but dragging 1 in 508 rise to Sileby, it was another matter. To achieve a speed well into the 60s before Leicester, No 5264 or one of her sisters would be sent storming away with the regulator wide open and the screw at something like 45% for accelerating, and never much less than 30% even at speed. The noise was impressive: the signalman at Barrow undoubtedly heard us coming, even in winter with the windows shut in his box, before he could see us on the easy curves, and we would be doing no more than 47 or 48 when we passed him. But the Class 5s seemed to thrive on it. Later, on the accelerated timings, this train became the 5.48 out of Derby, and the 5X which worked the 12.30pm from St Pancras took it back.

Just as an aside, there were occasions when the London 5X was failed on Derby shed, and then some odd combinations were turned out — a Compound and a Class 2P, or a 2P and a Belpaire, even one night an old Midland Class 2P on its own when the deputising train engine, a Compound, itself failed at the last minute and left the pilot engine to it. The less said about *that* trip, the better!

In performance there was little noticeable difference between the low-superheat, domeless engines and the later engines with high superheat, sloping throatplate boilers. They were draughted correctly from the start, and while the coal consumption of the low superheat engines was higher, as one would expect — tests in 1935 showed this to be of the order of 20% — they would steam well. That was the difference from the 'Jubilees', which in their early form did not have the blastpipe/chimney proportions right.

Apart from the superheater, however, one other important change was needed in the early days. The 1in thick frames on the first batches were not sufficiently robust, nor were they adequately stayed, and they suffered early cracking at the horn gaps. Later builds were provided with $1\frac{1}{16}$in frames and finally $1\frac{1}{8}$in frames were standardised post-war, together with Horwich hornstays.

The original Stanier spring gear, with screwed links in compression, was also far from ideal, particularly so on a two-cylinder locomotive which generated a fair amount of coupled axlebox knock. Besides, like most 4-6-0s the Class 5s tended to settle down at the back end after a few months, due to loss of spring camber and the weight transfer from the drawbar pull, and by that time the adjusting nuts on the spring links were usually seized solid anyway. So in extreme cases you would get no more than $\frac{3}{4}$in clearance above the trailing coupled boxes, instead of the designed $1\frac{1}{2}$in, and with track irregularities and the like the boxes would start banging on the top of the horn gap and hammering home the message that the enginemen were getting a rough ride.

The coupled boxes themselves were whitemetalled on the horn faces, with brass wearing strips riveted to the guide flanges. This was a fine box for freedom from heating, but there was no denying that appreciable knock did develop in the horns at the then normal shopping mileages of

70,000 or thereabouts, and that lateral clearances could become excessive due to wear, looseness and sometimes complete loss of the brass strips. It was the use of manganese steel liners on Timken cannon roller bearing boxes that sparked off the idea of using them on plain bearing axleboxes to obviate this trouble, and so some early 4800-series engines were so equipped. The form of the application still left something to be desired — the liners on the boxes were in channel form, fillet-welded round the edges and plug-welded to the face of the box — and could not be kept solid to the box due to slight 'spring'. The design was therefore changed subsequently to a three-piece liner, the flanges being separate, and the main section was attached by fillet welding at the edges and in holes about $1\frac{1}{4}$ in diameter on the face. This anchored them extremely well. The guide liners were welded to a mild steel backing plate which was bolted to the axlebox guides, and permitted shimming at works repair.

At depots where tyre wear was moderate, either because of the nature of the work (freight work caused more tyre wear than passenger) or some characteristic of the area, these manganese steel linered boxes ran some phenomenal mileages without attention other than keeping the underkeep clean and pad in good order. Perth shed was a classic in this respect, for a batch of new Class 5s there in the late 1940s all ran over 150,000 miles to first intermediate repair, and one did well over the 200,000mile mark before going to St Rollox. We could find no more rational explanation for this than the lubricating value of Scotch mist in preventing flange wear on the curves of the Highland main line!

As a result of this experience, it was apparent that there was an excellent case for retrospective fitting of manganese steel liners to all earlier Class 3s, and the financial authority for so doing also included the welding-in of new frame inserts $1\frac{1}{8}$ in thick at the horn gaps to suit the simple Horwich horn clips, and a changeover from the original screwed links in compression where fitted, to solid, cottered tension spring links.

The latter were a delightfully simple, foolproof device. All screwed links suffered from seizure of the adjusting nuts, and often at works repair had to be burned off. The cottered links were straight forgings of rectangular section, with a milled slot at each end, into which fitted flat cotters, with shoulders to stop them working out, bearing on the spring end shoe and the follower for the auxiliary rubber springs. The cotters were available in a range of widths, and by suitable selection at the weigh-table (changing of cotters was done using miniature hydraulic jacks) the weight adjustment and clearance above axleboxes could be obtained. It became standard practice to set the engine high on the trailing axleboxes, with about $1\frac{7}{8}$ in clearance above them, so that as it settled it would come down to something like the design figure of $1\frac{1}{2}$ in, and lose little more over an extended period. Fig 2 shows a typical arrangement.

All went well until a new batch of Class 5s, built at Horwich, were sent

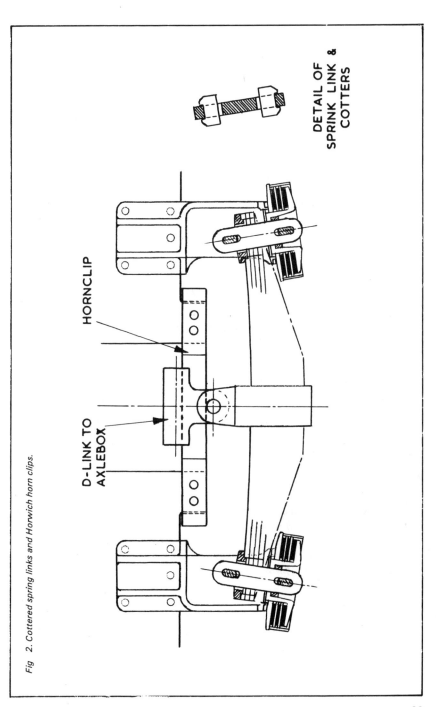

Fig 2. Cottered spring links and Horwich horn clips.

HORNCLIP

D-LINK TO
AXLEBOX

DETAIL OF
SPRINK LINK &
COTTERS

39

to Scotland, and Nos 4796 and 4797 went to Perth. Right from the start they were in trouble. On the Glasgow-Aberdeen expresses the drivers within a matter of weeks reported them 'rough riding', and it transpired that this was due to heavy axlebox knock rather than any liveliness as a vehicle. Out came the long feeler gauges, and the axlebox guide clearances were found to be correct. I was sent to Scotland to see what it was all about, and it was laid on that No 4797 should be available for me on the 10.0am from Buchanan Street to Aberdeen.

On a grey, damp November day, therefore, I introduced myself to a dour old Perth driver at Buchanan Street, and satisfied his curiosity as to my purpose in riding with him. 'Oh, aye, they're rough', he confirmed, 'ye'll soon see for yeself'.

I did. Before we had gone more than 50yds I knew exactly what we were in for. There was a hard, metallic 'bang', apparently in the left trailing coupled box, once every revolution of the wheel, with a minor 'clank' in between. You could feel the footplate shudder under your feet every time, and the coal dust and small spillage on the footboards danced as each thump went through you, rattling the cab doors and loosening the front window catches.

It was bad enough slogging up the 1 in 78 past St Rollox — there were not many worse starts for a cold engine than the one out of Buchanan Street — but once on the main line at Glenboig, when we really started to run, it became pandemonium. As we went round the curves down Cumbernauld Glen full tilt, with speed nudging the 70 mark, there was utter bedlam on the footplate and the driver was glancing at me out of the corner of his eye as if to say 'Had enough?' But I maintained a broad grin, so far as I could with teeth chattering uncontrollably from the vibration, and told him with my eyes (speech was impossible) that I was all right if he was. Later on, we tried her on all combinations of regulator opening and cutoff, and when coasting, and found little difference when the regulator was open, though it was worse on the main valve than on the pilot, and was largely unaffected by cutoff. A return trip on No 4796 in the afternoon — on which, incidentally, a gauge glass burst near Gleneagles, perhaps as a result of the vibration — confirmed that the trouble was not confined to one engine.

I came back and rode with a Crewe North engine of the same batch, No. 4789, and she did exactly the same. Since it was going to be easier to play about with her than with an engine working to Aberdeen and Inverness, this engine was selected for the attempt at a cure. We weighed up all the evidence — which included the fact that it was rare, but not unknown, for Crewe or Derby-built engines to show such symptoms — and all the possible causes (for instance there were four degrees of reciprocating balance on Class 5s — 40, 50, 55 and 66 per cent) and in the end boiled it down to valve setting.

Now the valve events of the Class 5s were just a little odd, if the motion arrangement drawing was to be believed. Remarkably, this showed the valve leads as .2735in at the front port and .2265in at the back port. Valve setting to half a thou', indeed! In practice, of course, it was done to much more robust standards! But Horwich Works had assumed, perhaps not unreasonably in the absence of further guidance, that these figures were specified to take account of heat expansion when working, and that if they set the valves to them, cold, everything would be all right on the night. It wasn't. In fact, the figures of lead were what the drawing office wanted under working conditions.

An attempt was made to evaluate the effects of expansion due to working temperatures: not easy, because one could only assume some of the temperatures, and had to assume, further, that the frames expanded forwards from the back cylinder flange due mainly to exhaust steam temperature; that the valve chests expanded evenly about the cylinder centreline due to something like superheat temperature; and that the valve spindle expanded forwards from the crosshead pin at a mixture of steam and exhaust temperatures. I cannot remember the revised figures now, but in one case they made about $\frac{3}{32}$in difference and they certainly appalled the chargehand on the section when we took No 4789 into Crewe works for the valves to be reset. He was one Leach by name, and when it came to departing from established practice, a leech by nature. It took two hours of patient, sometimes heated argument to persuade him to do it the way I wanted — and of course he did not believe it would work anyway.

But it did. I went out on several trips with that engine afterwards and she ran like a well-oiled sewing machine. One job we had, I recall, was to take a pickup goods from Stafford to Hadley Junction, make a trip up the Oakengates branch, and then bring a through freight back to Stafford. The driver, naturally, was curious to know why I should be riding on such a lowly job — which was part of a several-day cycle — and I did not entirely satisfy his curiosity. But coming back, with about 60 on, we slogged up from Donnington to Newport and then, on the easier stretch beyond, I told him to leave his regulator full open and pull her up on the reversing gear, just to see what would happen. He got her back to 25% and stopped turning. I cajoled, and he pulled her up to 20%. 'Go on, and see what she does', I requested.

He slowly wound her back until in the end we were bowling along on fairly level road with full regulator, the engine in mid-gear (checked for accuracy of the indicator in advance and, because of the lead port opening, actually meaning about 7% cutoff), an almost inaudible beat at the chimney, and not a sound of any sort from the axleboxes. The rail joints could be heard loud and clear. The driver just scratched the back of his head and said: 'Well, I'll be damned. I've never seen an engine behave like *that* before!'

After that we reset the valves on a number of 'black sheep' with success, though there was a Farnley Junction Class 5 that defied our efforts and had to be shopped for the purpose. As a follow-up to this work, kits of valve setting tackle were produced for use at a number of the major sheds to enable the Motive Power people to do the job themselves. Without such tackle there was always an element of doubt as to the accuracy of the job, particularly so far as the back valve head was concerned, because of access problems.

It was immediately after No 4789 had been put right that the interchange trials of 1948 were being planned. No 45253 from Llandudno Junction was selected to represent the Class 5s, as she had run the right mileage since her last shopping. She was transferred to Kentish Town for the purpose, and a motive power inspector rode with her to verify that she was all right. He reported with a long face — she had a fairly serious box knock. She was taken into Derby works for the valves to be reset according to the new gospel, and I rode on her on the 10.16 Derby-York and the 2.40pm back, with a delightful character from Derby, Ernie Twigg, at the regulator, and an inspector to see fair play.

Twigg was an absolute dab hand with a Class 5, a hard runner when the timebook demanded it but one who wasted nothing, and his fireman was a positive gem, clearly brought up the way Twigg wanted. He had a fire that was incandescent all over, and of moderate thickness: pressure was held between 215 and 225lb all the time, there was never anything more than a light haze at the chimney at any time and never — and I mean never — any blowing off. It was a joy to watch his controlled firing, and his anticipation of each station stop by shutting the damper just before Twigg shut the regulator, opening it again as he reached for the regulator handle to restart. Would that he could have been used in the training of all new entrants as firemen — and for many of those that were already firemen.

That was a beautiful engine, No 45253. There was nothing that she could not do if asked. We brought ten bogies back from York that afternoon, stopping at Pontefract, Rotherham, Sheffield, and Chesterfield. Of course, it was a rotten road as far as Sheffield, with subsidence slacks and permanent speed restrictions for junctions. As we waited in the platform at Sheffield for the 'right-away', the inspector said: 'Now, Ernest, let's see what she will do'. Twigg got her on the move, and after about 50yds pulled the gear up to 55%. Up went the regulator to the full open stop, and No 45253 went away like a shot out of a gun. About at Heeley, Twigg pulled her up further to 48%, and there she was left until we dived into Bradwell tunnel.

The exhaust injector was on continuously, though by no means on full delivery, and water was held dead steady an inch from the top nut of the gauge glass. Pressure never went outside the 220-225lb range, and the fireman had partially to close the damper to stop her blowing off. Barking at the hills on either side of the valley, we worked the 300ton train up to a steady 36mph on the continuous 1 in 100 rise, passing Dore & Totley in a few seconds over 9min. I calculated that we were turning out something like 1150 equivalent DBHP in the process.

Overall on that journey from York to Derby our water consumption averaged the very low figure of 21.8gal per mile, which would be equal to about 30lb. of coal per mile, well below normal. Such economy could only have come from expert firemanship, high superheat due to the maintenance of a white-hot fire, and skilled driving. After that, what a miserable exhibition of effort-saving and bad time-keeping was given in the actual interchange trials! Certainly the machine was in no way to blame. Any resemblance between the performance on the Great Central section, for instance, and what the engine could have done was purely coincidental.

Then there was No 44767, the Stephenson valve gear engine. The outside valve gear was designed rather surreptitiously, and fitted almost as a 'dare'. Its mechanical performance was not as good as the normal Walschaerts gear, particularly in the first year or two, and the engine sounded rather rough in the axleboxes, roller bearings notwithstanding. However, she was generally regarded as a 'strong' engine by drivers. I said in 1958 that I expected her to be converted to standard at the next general repair, but events proved me wrong, and she still retains her outside Stephenson gear as preserved.

The last major modification that must be referred to in connection with the Class 5s was the fitting of Caprotti poppet valve gear, and here it is necessary to differentiate between the main batch (Nos 44738-44757) and the last two (Nos 44686/7). The first batch, with inside drive, fell very short of expectations. As built they were extremely sluggish in acceleration and hard climbing, but once well on the move they would run like hares and coast with utter freedom as the poppet valves dropped off their seats and gave a full bypass facility. Now those characteristics were not what men were used to with Class 5s, and drivers immediately became disenchanted with the Caprottis. George Fisher was quickly involved with complaints from Bristol (Barrow Road) men about their total inability to keep time on the gruelling start from Temple Meads with 2½ miles at 1 in 67-90 from Lawrence Hill to Fishponds, and these complaints were soon proved to be fully justified.

The first modification to get over the trouble savoured a bit of sharp practice, in that new cutoff indicator plates were fitted to the reversing gear. We were certain at the time that the new plates were giving the drivers falsely short cutoffs, but a dynamometer car report on comparative tests with Caprotti, Stephenson and Walschaerts engines suggested that it was the original plates that were wrong and that this had merely been corrected by the fitting of the new plates. However, that did not allay drivers' misgivings about the Caprotti engines; they listened to the chimney top and felt that they were being conned. In time, various cambox modifications were made to evaluate different valve events, and eventually these brought tolerable performance, though not by any means up to piston valve standards.

My first experience of this came one night on the 7.00pm Class C goods from Camden to Manchester. We had No 44749 on a train of 35 wagons, fully fitted, and on the rise to Tring on the slow road we received constant checks from a train in front. After each one, the driver really had to flog the engine away, and it was painful work getting up to about 30mph. Then, just as if some governor cut out at that speed, the engine would really begin to get hold of the train, and full regulator and 25% cutoff would keep us rolling at 45-50mph up the 1 in 335. At Roade, after a lengthy wait for other trains, we at last got a clear road, and as we passed the box the signalman cryptically called to us that he was turning us out on the fast line about fifteen minutes ahead of the 'West Coast Postal'. The driver certainly took the hint, and the Caprotti showed us how, once on the move, she could show a clean pair of heels. The downhill stretch to Blisworth gave us the initial momentum without too much difficulty, and thereafter she kept up a steady 50-60mph almost all the way to the turnoff at Ashby Junction, Nuneaton, on full regulator, 25% cutoff, and a blinding fire maintained by an utterly staccato exhaust. It was an exhilarating experience to hear the engine tearing along in the darkness in this way.

You could see exactly the same characteristics in the log of a run published in the *Railway Magazine* in March 1966, involving No 44757 with a modest seven-coach train on the Settle & Carlisle line. Speeds on the rising start from Carlisle were abysmal — 28 at Petteril Bridge, and 37 at Scotby. The level stretch beyond Cumwhinton got speed up to 48, and the engine was by then getting hold of its train. Once over Low House 'hump' the impetus given by 1¼ miles down at 1 in 132 enabled her to then make excellent running, mainly between 62 and 72, on the rising road to Appleby and to climb creditably to Ais Gill with no speed lower than 43. That was fairly typical Caprotti behaviour.

The last two Caprotti Class 5s were a very different kettle of fish from the originals: further modifications to the valve events made them strong and lively, but in doing so their riding qualities were slightly impaired — not as a vehicle, but in their sweetness as a piece of machinery. They could suffer from axlebox knock, though in a much milder form than that of rogue piston valve locomotives, and to the best of my knowledge this was never fully bottomed.

Be under no illusions, however: the Caprotti gear was not adopted in an attempt to get better haulage performance or greater fuel economy. It was put on, in the labour-scarce post-war world, to extend still further the mileage between valve examinations, which with the piston-valve engines was 30-36,000miles. With the Caprotti cam-boxes and valves this was stepped up successfully to 40-48,000 miles, which phased nicely with the 20-24,000mile renewal of piston rings. The only mechanical trouble experienced, after doing a bit of development work, was a certain tendency for valves to stick if priming occurred, and this could lead to breakages.

Finally a word about the draughting of the Class 5s. The vast majority were built with plain single chimneys, with the early GW-type jumper blastpipes giving way in the late 1930s to plain fixed-orifice blastpipe caps 5¼in diameter. This gave excellent results, and steaming was free with almost any coal. Then there was a post-war period of trying double blastpipes and chimneys, and three piston-valve and five Caprotti engines were so fitted. E. S. Cox has said* that the double chimneys were 'incorrectly proportioned', but if so it was difficult to detect in service, for the ones that I rode on — both piston-valve and Caprotti — steamed extremely well and appeared to have the edge over the single chimneys when the coal was interior or the work particularly heavy.

To conclude, let me try to summarise the performance potential of these notable locomotives. In good hands and in reasonable condition, a figure of nearly 1,300 EDBHP emerges as a sort of concensus output sustainable for 20min, ie within the limits governing the mortgaging of the boiler. The literally continuous maximum output was of the order of 1,100 EDBHP. Such maxima were generally found in the 35-50mph range, as one would expect from a locomotive with a thoroughly modern front end and 6ft 0in wheels. As to maximum speed, 90mph was readily available on modest falling grades, or seven rev/sec of the coupled wheels.

To illustrate methods of working, I will instance a run made in 1958 on No 45279 on the Manchester-Derby line with a modest train of 203 tons tare, 215tons gross on 'Special Limit' timings. Up the long drag from Cheadle Heath to the south end of Disley Tunnel, mostly on 1 in 100-132, full regulator working with 35% cutoff was used, after an initial 30mph temporary speed restriction at Bramhall Moor Lane, and this was holding 42mph until we slipped on wet rail in the tunnel: before we recovered, we dropped to 40mph, which was then sustained. Similar handling from the Chinley restart produced a gradual rise to 41mph at Peak Forest on the 1 in 90 bank, requiring nearly 1,100 EDBHP. Steaming was quite steady, 215lb/sq in being held to Disley and nothing less than 210 lb/sq in at Peak Forest.

But perhaps the most interesting feature was the lightning acceleration from the Rowsley and Ambergate slacks. In each case full regulator and 30% cutoff were used right until steam was shut off for the station stops: in the first case this brought speed up from 52 to 76mph in under 3miles of gently falling grades, and in the second we accelerated from 30 to 80mph in about 7miles of similar easy grades. In the latter case pressure was allowed to fall from 215 to 205lb/sq in in the process, in readiness for the Derby station stop. Not much wrong with the engine or its handling there.

But to show just how great a machine the Class 5 was, I must refer to two published runs, both made in the twilight years of steam and with locomotive built nearly twenty years previously. Full details of the first

*Chronicles of Steam, page 153. Ian Allan, 1967.

will be found in the *Railway Magazine* for May 1967, and give an extreme demonstration of their speed capabilities; for the second, the *Railway Magazine* for March 1964 and subsequent correspondence in *Railway World* in 1973 deal with the ultimate in power output from a Class 5 for a fairly brief period.

Suffice it to say that No 44917, on a six-coach train of 215tons gross from Gobowen to Shrewsbury, covered the 18.0miles in 16min 15sec start-to-stop. In doing so, an average speed of 87.2mph was maintained over the 9.5miles of undulating road from Rednal to Leaton, with an intermediate maximum of 96 at milepost 119 and a further separate 90 below Leaton. There is no record of anything higher in speed in service — and this run was made in 1966!

We must go to Scotland in 1963 for the other, made by No 44970 on the 10.15am Glasgow (Buchanan Street) to Aberdeen, a seven-coach train of 265tons gross. So phenomenal was the performance that grave doubts were cast about its feasibility with a single Class 5, but calculations which I subsequently made showed this to be entirely within the capability of a single engine, by mortgaging the boiler for a relatively short period by no more than 3in of water level.

Briefly, Stirling was passed at a speed well above the 40mph limit, and the train was then accelerated very rapidly to 72 at Cornton, before tackling Kinbuck bank. By milepost 125¼, up 4¾ miles of 1 in 100 — 84 with brief stretches slightly steeper, speed had fallen to 58, but then on the remaining ¾ mile of slightly easier gradients speed recovered to 62 at Kinbuck. To do this, with full regulator working, must have required cutoffs of up to about 43%, and the power output was little, if any, less than 1,800 EDBHP. This was thrashing the engine unmercifully, and one can only wonder what caused the crew to make such a tremendous effort. But whatever it was, it enabled them to show what a remarkable machine they had in their hands. So little was the engine winded after Kinbuck that it was worked up to 82mph on the ensuing level road to Greenloaning!

This, then, was the Stanier Class 5, the enginemen's friend. They were pitted against B1 and 'Hall' in their own true power class in the interchange trials of 1948, and in subsequent service, But can you imagine either of those rising to such heights?

7/Pony Trucks to the Fore

The 2-6-0 mixed traffic locomotive has had a distinctly chequered career in Britain. After a false start with the American engines imported by several lines at the turn of the century and the GWR 'Aberdares' (all of which were strictly freight engines), the modern concept of a 2-6-0 with outside cylinders came in with the GWR (1911), GNR (1912) and LB&SCR (1913), followed by others later. This trend continued through the 1920s on all the post-grouping railways, but in the 1930s there was an increasing preference for a leading bogie as more suitable for the high speeds that a modern front end allowed — witness the 'Halls', Class 5s and others. Undoubtedly the sad experience with the 2-6-4 tank *River Cray* at Sevenoaks in 1927 conditioned thinking to some extent in this respect.

Following World War II, however, a new situation arose. The increasing age of the smaller end of the locomotive fleets, largely confined to secondary and branch line duties, its frequent unsuitability for mixed traffic work, and its lack of labour-saving servicing features prompted the LMS to produce a new range of locomotives to handle such jobs. The need for adequate adhesion and brake power within modest axleloads and short overall length made the 2-6-0 tender engine a natural choice in this field. The value of this choice was soon emphasised when the LMS designs were adopted, following nationalisation, for use on many other parts of the railway system, thus incidentally forestalling the powers that be at Doncaster, who were working up a rather similar project in the form of a scaled-down Class K1 which would have been about 2½MT.

The first of the new designs was the little Ivatt Class 2 2-6-0, which began to appear late in 1946 together with its tank engine derivative. It was just after this that I came home finally from Army service in India to find these little 6400s and 1200s appearing. It was then a rather novel idea to see a brand-new design produced for stopping passenger and branch mixed traffic duties, though curiously enough, in India I had seen quite a bit of this, with such unusual designs as outside-cylindered Caprotti 2-4-2 tanks. The 6400s were built down to a weight restriction of 14tons axleload, with wheels of only 5ft 0in diameter but fully adequate, with a good front end, to get up to 70mph any time for the asking. They were provided with all convenience and comfort for the crew, were entirely suitable for unbraked freight trains, and had the built-in mechanical endurance to run 100,000 miles between shoppings with only routine maintenance.

I do not think I can recall a class of locomotive which was so immediately and universally accepted by enginemen. They welcomed both the tender and tank versions with open arms, they worshipped the very rails they stood on — men who had staggered around the branches with Midland Class 2s and 0-6-0s, men used to L&YR radial tanks, or men weaned on L&NWR 'Cauliflowers'.

For the first 18 months or so they were very carefully watched over by the Mechanical Inspectors, especially the Kettering and Goole allocations and those working the CK&P line. It was necessary to reduce the blastpipe cap diameter slightly to ensure reliable steaming, and new, smaller injector cones were fitted because the 'Monitor' injectors were tending to swamp the boiler. But the overall result was an engine that could be driven hard, fired with a few bits of coal through which you could nearly see the grate, and that would steam well enough to suit the most fastidious engineman.

At least, we thought so until the Western Region, offered the type for future use instead of building more Dean 0-6-0s, took No 6413 for trial. I think that if Crewe had had the foresight to make a copper cap for the chimney before she went, the verdict from Swindon would have been a lot different. As it was, they alleged that she would not steam, she would not pull, and she would not do anything else that a Dean Goods could (except, maybe, keep the weather off the crew). Anyway, they made a new chimney for her — no copper cap, however — and proceeded to put her through her paces under the now-famous controlled conditions. Certainly the performance was spectacular.

I remember S.O. Ell telling me of the Operating authorities' reaction to his proposals as the tests developed. When, finally, he asked for a 15coach train, they asked him whether he was really serious, and were most reluctant to let him loose with such a load for a small engine for fear of stopping the main line. But the little 2-6-0, working right up to the limit of her boiler output at 14,000lb of steam an hour, came home triumphantly. On the return journey from near Bristol to Swindon, she worked this big train up into the 60s at Stoke Gifford and then stormed up the 10½ miles of 1 in 300 to Badminton at a minimum of 40mph with boiler pressure and water level maintained and everything going swimmingly. I fancy William Dean would have scratched his head about that one! I was working for E. S. Cox at the time, and when, with some traces of excitement and pride, he told me what No 6413 had just managed, I laughingly suggested to him that, given larger tenders, we at last had *the* machine for working the 'Royal Scot'.

But small though these little 2-6-0s were, they had a beautifully proportioned boiler, with a fairly deep firebox with little slope on the grate. So firing needed no high degree of sophistication nor strenuous

1 *(Top)* The engine that started it all — No 45671 *Prince Rupert*. Here seen at Manchester Victoria in a steady drizzle in March, 1956, with paintwork gleaming and motion burnished to work a Royal Train from the Grand National at Aintree. Note the Newton Heath set of turned and polished buffers and polished screw coupling fitted for the occasion./*Author*

2 *(Above)* 'Claughton' 4-6-0 No 5964 *Patriot* on up Manchester express at Bletchley in June 1931. Note the GC Robinson tender transferred from an ROD 2-8-0./*P. Ransome-Wallis.*

3 *(Above)* Down 'Royal Scot' express leaving Rugby about 1929, headed by 'Royal Scot' 4-6-0 No 6134 *Atlas.* Rugby No 5 box is on the left, and 'The Block', referred to in the text, is on the extreme right. Both have now disappeared./*Locomotive Publishing Co.*

4 *(Below)* Derby Works: the wheel balancing machine. The wheels being run — with weights on crankpins equivalent to coupling and connecting rods — are the drivers of a Class 2P 4-4-0 after retyring, though this was not normal practice./*Crown Copyright*

5 *(Above)* Derby Works: No 2 bay of the Erecting Shop in September 1938./*British Railways, Collection J M Jarvis*

6 *(Below)* Derby Works: Class 4F 0-6-0 No 4260 under construction in the Erecting Shop, 1926. Note the small piston valves with very indirect ports, the narrow axlebox guides, and the plates to which the buffer beam channels were bolted./*Crown Copyright*

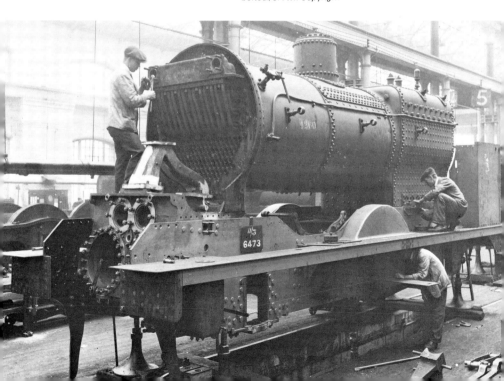

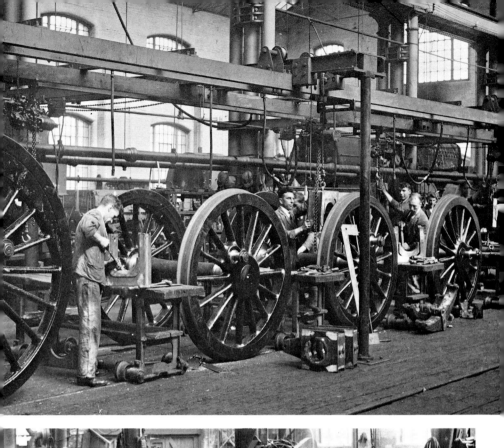

7 *(Above left)* Derby Works: Axlebox bedding area in No 2 bay, Erecting Shop, 1929. The man in the foreground is scraping the loose brass of a Midland steel axlebox. This type is also being bedded to the next two pairs of wheels. Suspended from the air hoist above the fourth pair is a manganese bronze box./*British Railways, Collection J M Jarvis*

8 *(Left)* Derby Works: Cylinder moulds and cores in the Iron Foundry. In the foreground, the mould for the slide-valve cylinders for an 0-6-0 takes shape; behind, the cores for piston valve chests and ports for a Class 2P 4-4-0 await the mould. Note the tortuous steam ports and the narrow exhaust passages to pass between the cylinder barrels./*Crown Copyright*

9 *(Above)* A Compound reduced to lowly duties: No 41185 leaves Derby on a stopping train to Lincoln in 1954. Note the deeper front-end frames./*Author*

10 *(Right)* The cab of 'Jubilee' No 5714 as built. The sand gun above the firehole doors was subsequently removed. Note the quadrant type damper controls on the floor on the fireman's side./*Crown Copyright*

11 *(Above)* Bogie of a 'Duchess' Pacific. Note the side bolster 'spittoons'. The coils of a side check spring are just visible above the near wheel./*Crown Copyright*

12 *(Below)* Class 5MT 4-6-0 No 45173 climbing towards Killin Junction with the 12.12 pm Glasgow (Buchanan Street) to Oban in May 1955. The engine carries the original type of domeless, straight throat-plate boiler: note the white feather at the safety valves./*W. J. V. Anderson*

13 *(Above)* Class 5MT 4-6-0 45253 on
Millhouses Shed. This was the engine used for
the 1948 Interchange Trials in
England./*D. Perrey*

14 *(Below)* What made a Class 5 so fleet of
foot!/*M. S Welch*

15 *(Below)* Ivatt Class 2MT 2-6-0 46448 on Stafford Shed in August 1959./*J. B. Bucknall*

16 *(Bottom)* Ivatt Class 4MT 2-6-0 No 43027 leaving St Pancras on a trial, 7 May 1952. The original double chimney has been replaced with a fabricated chimney having the internal dimensions of that subsequently adopted as standard./*P. Ransome-Wallis*

17 *(Right)* ... and for what? No 43035, with standard single chimney, passes Clifton & Lowther on an undemanding ballast train./*Eric Treacy*

18 *(Below right)* Horwich 2-6-0 No 42895 on Holbeck shed, 16 April 1961. Curiously, her driving wheels are of Stanier pattern with triangular rims and built-up balance weights. She also carries power class 5 only./*G. M. Morrison*

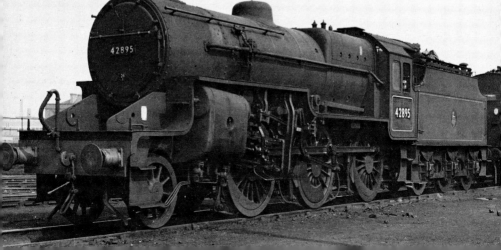

19 *(Above)* Reidinger Rotary valve gear on 2-6-0 No 42829./*B. E. Morrison*

20 *(Below)* 'Patriot' 4-6-0 No 5538 on Derby Shed, 13 March 1938. Allocated to Leeds, she was soon afterwards named *Giggleswick*./*H. Russell*

21 *(Top)* 'Jubilee' 4-6-0 No 5552, with domeless boiler, nearly new and unnamed, in 1934. This engine was renumbered 5642 when that engine was specially prepared in black and chrome livery and named *Silver Jubilee*./P. Ransome-Wallis

22 *(Above)* 'Jubilee' 4-6-0 No 45580 *Burma* on Newton Heath shed in March 1956. She retained a straight throatplate boiler, but now fitted with separate dome and topfeed./*Author*

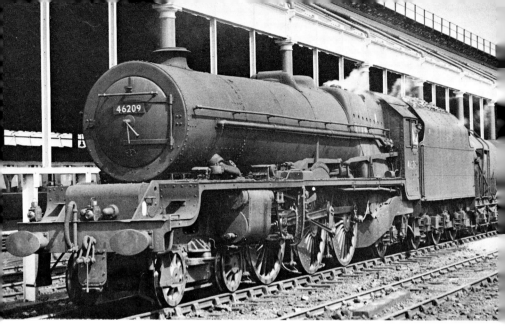

23 (Above) 'Princess' 4-6-2 No 46209 *Princess Beatrice* pauses at Rugby on humble duty, the 11.53am Class C Euston to Crewe, in August 1961, shortly before withdrawal. The buttress strip on the frame in front of the cylinder flange is just visible./*Ian Allan Library*

24 (Below) 'Princess' 4-6-2 No 46205 *Princess Victoria* on an up Anglo-Scottish express near Elvanfoot. Note the massive motion girder casting in connection with the rocker gear to the inside piston valves./*Eric Treacy*

25 *(Above)* A 'Duchess' in water trouble. No 46230 *Duchess of Buccleugh* stops out of course to put the bag in at Beattock Summit on the up ''Royal Scot''. With Strawfrank troughs under repair, after 52 miles of steady climbing and with 42 miles to go to the troughs at Mossband, the driver was unwilling to risk it./*Eric Treacy*

26 *(Below)* The last 'Duchess', No 46257 *City of Salford*, pulls out of Liverpool Lime Street with a Euston train. Note the rear cast steel truck and full-length raking doors on the side of the ashpan./*Eric Treacy*

27 *(Top)* Beyer-Garratt No 4990./*P. Ransome-Wallis*   **28** *(Above)* Fowler Class 7F 0-8-0 No 9508./*LPC*

29 *(Top)* Stanier Class 8F 2-8-0 No 48060 on
Gloucester Shed, 12 April 1965. Note the star on
the cab side indicating 50 per cent balancing of
reciprocating masses in the coupled
wheels./*P. L. Simpson*

30 *(Above)* WD 2-8-0 No 90595, fitted with
miniature snowplough, on Holbeck Shed, 6 July
1961. The five-feed coupled axlebox oilboxes
above the footframing, and the tender spring
equalising beams, are clearly
visible./*G. W. Morrison*

31 *(Above)* Fowler 2-6-4 tanks under construction at Derby Works, 29 August 1929. Note the open-top cast steel smokebox saddle. The cylinder lying on the floor behind shows the extension through the frames into the saddle for steam and exhaust passages, which was normal Derby practice of the time./*Crown Copyright*

32 *(Below)* Fowler 2-6-4T No 42322 on Newton Heath shed in June 1959. She had received by this time the Stanier-type smokebox saddle and external steam pipes./*J. E. Wilkinson*

effort by the fireman. He just had to put six to eight shovelsful at a time round the box, and the engine would buzz along with the pressure gauge needle nudging the red line. They were, of course, too small to be a 'first valve' engine for the driver, except under favourable circumstances, and part-main valve and 20-30% cutoff were quite normal working methods.

One train on which I rode regularly was the 6.00pm. Derby-Burton local, which was normally worked by a 1200 class tank, but sometimes produced one of the tender engines. It ran all stations and usually loaded to four non-corridors. This section is to all intents dead level. From Pear Tree to Repton, and then on to Burton, the Burton men would cane them away from the stations, and gradually pull them back to about 20% cutoff, with the regulator fully open or nearly so. This would have the train up to 60mph between stations, which were about 4½ miles apart.

Maintenance was remarkably light. A minor contretemps arose with cab doors on the tender engines, which did not allow for sufficient relative movement between engine and tender on some sharp siding curves — Darlaston was one place where this arose — and they would burst open when the squeeze was put on them; this was easily cured by a small reduction in door width. One should mention also the extreme cleanliness of the valves and pistons. At 30-36,000mile examination they came out as clean as when they were put in, with the machining marks still visible and negligeable wear. The examination mileage was therefore stepped up so that they required no more than a single opening-up for examination between shoppings at up to 100,000miles.

With these new engines successfully launched and adopted with acclaim by enginemen, 1947 saw the emergence of the larger Class 4 2-6-0s, beginning with No 3000. Alas, in their first form they were not the immediate success of their smaller sisters, nor did they ever fully become so. For that, a modicum of blame could be attached, believe it or not, to the Midland Railway. Its influence died hard!

The boiler was an entirely new design, and was excellently proportioned so far as the tubes, superheater and free gas areas were concerned. I recall watching the tests of the first boilers for this class in Crewe Works and thinking that such a chubby boiler should be just the thing for making steam. I knew, too, that before finalising the design of these engines, Derby had been sufficiently influenced by the US Army 2-8-0s to scheme out a 2-6-0 with a wide firebox boiler high above the coupled wheels. (A good deal of interest was shown — and some bore fruit — in these US 2-8-0s on the LMS). But the grate was very steeply inclined, at a slope of about 1 in 4, the same as on the Class 4F 0-6-0 — this in 1947! — and quite a lot of trouble resulted from this.

Three innovations were also incorporated, all of which were unsuccessful and had to be removed. One was the double blastpipe and chimney, the latter positively enormous and quite disproportionate in relation to the size of the locomotive. A unique feature was that the centre-lines of the two exhaust jets were inclined, in vee formation, giving a very direct and compact blastpipe. The second was the use on a large scale of steel piping instead of the more normal copper, much of it clipped under the boiler-mounted foot-framing. The third was the adoption of Klinger reflex water gauges — another result of the experience with the American engines coupled with some unfortunate experiences with the standard (ex-Midland) gauge glass protector.

The grate inclination and double chimney between them made the steaming uniformly dismal rather than erratic. With the double chimney they had to be fired particularly carefully, since if they were working heavily the blast would pull the fire down the steep slope of the grate, aided by gravity and any vibration due to the engine's speed, piling it up in a great mound reaching to the underside of the brick arch. It all functioned rather like a slow jigger-feed on a coaling plant! The fireman had to learn to fire next to nothing down to the front of the box, but just keep putting the coal inside the door and in the back corners, and let the front of the grate feed itself from there. Even then it was only partially successful, as George Fisher and I found to our cost one morning on a trip on a mineral train from Rowsley to Gowhole. So off came the double chimneys, to be replaced by conventional single ones. This made the steaming reasonably satisfactory provided that firing was directed to preventing build-up under the arch.

The steel piping was all ripped off and replaced by copper at the first general repair, because of the incidence of fractures due to vibration and relative movement between boiler and frames. The water gauges, too, were soon replaced by standard tubular gauges, for the LM's softened water took the serrations off the water side of the flat gauge glasses very quickly, nullifying the clear silver/black distinction between steam and water to the point where it was almost impossible to see the water level at all.

For me, personally, they were most uncomfortable engines to ride on in my usual stance behind the driver, because the tender cab roof was rather low to sit below the back of the locomotive cab roof, and being fairly tall I was in a perpetual state of 'knees bend'. But for the normal crew they were fine.

The Class 4s had all the modern features adopted by Ivatt — manganese steel axlebox liners, cottered tension spring links, rocking grate and hopper ashpan, self-cleaning smokebox and so forth — and soon showed themselves very satisfactory mechanically, with tyre wear the only real limiting factor in deciding the need for shopping. There was a bit of axlebox knock trouble in the early days — Horwich build and valve setting again — but with suitable guidance from HQ this was soon overcome, as it had been on the Class 5s. From the drivers' point of view I think it would be fair to say that they appreciated their convenience and comfort, regarded them as a better tool for passenger work than a Class 4F 0-6-0, but inferior for real slogging freight work.

Then at the top end of the range there were the 245 Horwich 2-6-0s, affectionately known as 'Crabs', and their 40 taper boiler sisters. Before the advent of the Stanier Class 5 4-6-0s, they were used as general purpose, first-line mixed traffic engines, but once No 5020 had shown her capabilities they were relegated largely to secondary duties and because of their 19-20ton axleloads these duties could not be on many of the branch lines: they had to stay on the main lines and watch the Class 5s do the job which *they* had been doing.

Of the taper boiler version I have no first hand experience. They lived rather unexciting lives, for the most part between the limits of Stafford, Crewe, Liverpool and North Wales, and were only used for anything other than freight work when the going was hard for the shedmaster. They had a reputation for indifferent steaming, and I can well believe it from the boiler proportions: the small tubes, at 2in diameter, were much too big for their length, and clearly would have given excessive temperatures and heat loss at the smokebox end. They had a reputation for getting run down quickly, but on regular freight work that was not entirely surprising. I was always impressed, when studying the mechanical casualty statistics (anything which, due to locomotive causes, results in delaying a passenger train 5min or more, or a freight train 10min or more, constitutes a casualty) to see their remarkably good record, but this was hardly surprising in view of the very mundane work done by this quite modern design.

The origin of the parallel boiler engines, as is well known, was a continuation of Hughes' later lines of thought at Horwich, but they suffered a certain amount of 'Midlandisation' in the way of fittings, tender, etc., before they appeared after the grouping. Ungainly machines the 'Crabs' may have been in appearance, but they seemed to inspire tremendous confidence in the powers that be, who steadily upgraded their power classification from the original 4P5F to 5MT and then, in the mid-1950s, to 6P5F — all without any alterations to them otherwise.

Perhaps I may be permitted here to digress about power classification systems. The Midland scheme, which the LMS adopted — not surprisingly with Anderson still in charge — took no account of proved performance at all, but grouped all engines according to nominal tractive effort. In addition, a freight engine, for reasons best known to those who invented the system, was allowed to take 10% more tonnage on passenger trains (timed at 'Full Load' timings) than a passenger engine of the same numerical classification. For instance, between Derby and Birmingham, a fairly level road, a Class 2P 4-4-0 was allowed 270 tons, a Compound (Class 4P) was permitted 360 tons, while a Class 4F 0-6-0, being a freight engine, was allowed 10% more, or 396 tons. Now both the Class 2P and the Class 4F used the 'G7S' boiler interchangeably, and as every schoolboy knows, the limiting factor in power output over about 15-20mph is the boiler, and nothing to do with tractive effort. If anything, the Class 4F should have taken *less* than the Class 2P, because of the additional internal engine friction arising from greater rotational speeds.

After nationalisation, it was found necessary to devise a new system which would take account of the various influencing factors other than tractive effort, in order to suit the whole fleet. On this basis the 'Crab' came within the Class 5 category for passenger work, although a little inferior to the Class 5 4-6-0 — just as one might expect. But the LM Region had a serious shortage of locomotives of Class 6 and above, due to a barely coherent policy of building medium-sized engines and in general replacing like for like (so far as power was concerned), and this would have been a theoretical embarrassment for weekend excursion work. So the system was cut through completely in the case of the 'Crabs' by classifying them 6P5F, as a result of which they were expected on "Full Load" passenger timings to take the same loadings as a 'Jubilee' or 'Clan'. Why this should be so, when the grate and firebox were smaller than on a Class 5, and the boiler barrel and free gas area were generally smaller, defies explanation. Everyone knew that a 'Crab' was not in Class 6P and never would be.

Be that as it may, within their true capacity they were no mean machine and quite a popular one with enginemen, especially for fitted freight work. In fact, except for the fully fitted (now Class 6) freights, and particularly on heavily-graded lines which involved some real slogging, many men preferred a 'Crab' to a Class 5. There was more sheer brute strength in them, which in certain circumstances gave them the edge over their more modern sisters. Some of the jobs over Peak Forest, such as the various night part-fitted freights between Rowsley and the Manchester yards, showed them up under ideal working conditions. On the passenger side, they did an enormous amount of summer excursion work, as anyone looking at the Blackpool sheds on a Saturday lunchtime would know. On the old Central Division of the LM Region, indeed, they did a fair amount of passenger work all the year round, though not on fast services. They did it competently and efficiently, though in a lumbering sort of way.

At the time of the 'Crabs' building they were mechanically in advance of their contemporaries, but subsequent developments under Stanier left them rather behind. Their proportions were good, they were a simple, rugged machine, and yet nobody could say they were all an engine should be. Take the coupled axleboxes, for example. They were of generous size, and should have been the equal of the Stanier box for reliability, yet few engines needed more careful nursing while running-in if hot boxes were to be avoided, and throughout their life they were liable to cause trouble. The underkeeps were very cramped, and the pad seemed incapable of holding the fort in the event of the oil supply being interrupted. (On the later Stanier/Ivatt engines the oil supply from the mechanical lubricator was put direct into the underkeep and the whole lubrication of the journal was done by the pad from that source). So hot boxes were no rarities with 'Crabs'.

The 'Crab' injectors — a Midland live steam one and an exhaust steam type on the fireman's side — were even more touchy than on most locomotives of LMS design. The feed regulator mechanism to the exhaust injector was a mess, located as it was in a pocket in the dragbox under the cab floor that filled up with coal dust and spillage, which inevitably caused it to jam. The water feed from the tender suffered all the same disadvantages as on the 'Patriots' and 'Jubilees' afflicted with the Fowler 3,500gallon tender — endless sieve trouble from leaves, small coal (many had the tank vent pipes in the middle of the bunker) and other rubbish. Furthermore, when they were demoted to a mixture of freight and shunting work, as many were, it hammered the reliability out of the exhaust injector, which could only be used intermittently and suffered from the automatic changeover feature as the regulator was constantly opened and shut. If the mechanical foreman was wise, he would blank off the actuating pipe and let the thing work on live steam only.

A curious feature of the 'Crab' was the very substantial fall in water level in the boiler when the regulator was closed. All engines did this to some extent, of course, and about 1½in drop was normal, but these engines would drop more than most. The result was that on the steeply graded lines of the old Central Division — and particularly on the East Lancashire lines, where there were whole series of gables — this led to more than average lead plug trouble. This was particularly so at weekends, when engines not exactly in the pink were put on heavy excursion trains with less experienced firemen, who were so preoccupied with holding pressure while belting up the hills, if necessary at the expense of water level, that they were taken by surprise when they passed the summits and started down the other side and the driver shut off.

The riding of the 'Crabs' was generally pretty good, but it was necessary to keep the coupled spring position under careful control. These springs were distinctly on the weak side, and the rough track in a lot of yards did not exactly help, so that when the engine settled down as mileage built up they could get uncomfortably rough and quite unfit for passenger work.

The five poppet-valve engines within the class showed no real superiority in performance over the piston valve engines, and because they were later coming up for development they never reached the stage when the valve mileage could be increased for examinations. In their original form with Lentz RC valve gear, they could be a real nuisance to drivers, because of the finite cutoff steps which were all that were available: no fine adjustment meant more regulator adjustment and problems in getting a right combination when working hard. But the fitting of the Reidinger infinitely variable gear in 1953 got over that difficulty.

Until the repair staff learned to appreciate their little idiosyncracies, however, they could cause some funny incidents. When the engines were at Saltley, more than one was reassembled after valve and piston examination only to see-saw gently when given steam — one side in forward gear and the other in something like back gear, due to incorrect phasing of the driving shafts on their splines. Fun such as this was also to be had when one ran a hot leading or driving box away from home, and despite elaborate precautions it was easy to get the shafts coupled up incorrectly after the necessary attention.

I had a trip on No 42822 one morning in its Reidinger valve gear days on a partially-fitted freight (then Class D, now Class 7) from Washwood Heath to Gloucester, loaded to 39 and a brake. Surprisingly, this train was routed via the platforms at Birmingham New Street rather than taking the more normal Camp Hill route, and we slogged up through the tunnels from New Street to Church Road Junction, mostly at 1 in 80, at about 10mph, on full regulator and 45-50% cutoff. In complete contrast, on the faintly falling grades from Stoke Works Junction to Eckington, speed was kept between 38 and 45 with the main valve of the regulator about half open and 16% cutoff. For the roughly 1 in 300 rise from Ashchurch to Cheltenham, the regulator went up to the stop with 25% cutoff, and this was enough to take us over the hump at a minimum of 22mph. Steaming was as near perfect as one could wish for. Water consumption worked out at 45.1 gal/mile: nothing very different from a piston valve engine, and equating to about 59lb of coal per mile.

But full regulator and 25% cutoff never got a 'Crab' out of Rowsley yard and up 15miles of 1 in 100/90 to Peak Forest with 45 loads on her tail, as old Rowsley, Heaton Mersey and Newton Heath drivers would tell you. The allowance for a fully fitted freight was 37min from a standing start, which meant working up to, and holding, 25mph on 1 in 90. The screw was not far back from full gear, the fireman didn't get a lot of time to survey the beauties of the Peak District, and there was no need to shut off the exhaust injector from time to time. More than likely he was wondering how much he dare put the other one on as well!

8/ 'Patriots' and 'Jubilees'

The LMS was always rather preoccupied with building medium-sized passenger locomotives. The nature of the passenger timetable in the 1930s, which was only just beginning — under the influence of increasing competition — to emerge from a long spell of mediocrity so far as speed were concerned, certainly encouraged this, as did the financial juggling associated with the annual locomotive renewal programme. So it was that, on a system with long-haul main lines, many of which cried out for sustained steaming of a high order if services were to be improved, the LMS finished its days with a quite unbalanced fleet of passenger locomotives, comprising at the upper end of the range 50 Pacifics, 81 'Royal Scots' and reboilered 5XPs, and 233 'Patriots' and 'Jubilees' remaining as 5XP. What is more, as late as 1950, when submitting its locomotive building and condemnation proposals to the then Railway Executive, the LM Region insisted that it could not justify rebuilding any more 'Patriots' with 2A boilers because, it claimed, there was no operating need for more big engines.

Even within the 233 engines of Class 5XP, the 44 unrebuilt 'Patriots' were hardly in the same street at the 189 'Jubilees'. They had been eclipsed by the sheer weight of numbers of their taper-boiler sisters. It is my lasting regret that I did not have the opportunity to ride in them during the brief prewar period when they were on real top-link work. Such 'Patriot' trips as I did have after the war were on very inferior work, bacause the whole class (except for one) were kept on the Western Division and very largely restricted to semi-fitted freight and stopping passenger trains. Only on busy summer Saturdays, or in emergency, were they seen on any top-class jobs.

But they did run them before the war. I used to see them on two particular jobs in those days, and rode on innumerable occasions behind 'Patriots' on one of them, the 11.17am Rugby to Euston. A queer train, that was. It used to wander up from Manchester, stopping at all sorts of odd spots on the way to Rugby, and after that did a bright sprint to Euston, calling at Blisworth and running the 62.8 miles from there in 61min start-to-stop. With the normal load of eight bogies it was money for jam for a 'Patriot', and she would keep up a steady 70-80mph all the way except for the last few miles up to Tring, and roll into Euston with a few minutes in hand.

There used to be a Loco. Inspector at Rugby, whose name now escapes me, about whom a legend was current that he had climbed on the engine one day, told the driver to ride the cushions and driven the engine himself, gaining 10min in the process. There was another story (no more vouched for than the first) that a fireman on this train had lost his shovel in the firebox soon after leaving Rugby and had fired the engine with his bare hands the rest of the way. Feasible, if arduous, with large lump coal: but it would have taken some doing with some of the small stuff and slack that was sometimes loaded on to tenders in the 1950s.

The other job which was the 'Patriots' prerogative was the fastest train on the LMS, the 6.20pm from Birmingham New Street to Euston, booked over the 65.1miles from Rugby to Watford in 60min start to stop. Now that did involve some hard running, again with loads of eight or nine bogies. The late Cecil J. Allen published details* of a run on this train on which No 5518 ran to Watford in 59min 41sec with a heavy 11 coach train of 355 tons gross, with intermediate speeds of 79 at Weedon, 68 minimum over Roade, 83½ at Castlethorpe — high by normal standards, this — nothing less than 60 over Tring, and a joyful 85 at Kings Langley.

From the many happy hours I spent in Clifton Road Junction box (demolished when Rugby was colour-light signalled in 1939) I can remember the sound of a 'Baby Scot' 'wuffling' out of Rugby on this job — they never roared like a 'Jubilee' did when it was really opened out — and bursting out from under the down Northampton line bridge in a flurry of steam, sound and blinding light as the fireman worked on his fire. Funnily enough, it was one evening in 1938 (if I recall correctly) that lingers best in my memory when there was no 'Patriot' on that 6.58pm out of Rugby. The clock had ticked away until 7.5pm before we were offered the train by Rugby No 1, and I had remarked to George, the bobby, that she must have been held up badly. We saw the column of steam silhouetted against the glare of the BTH neon lights as she came up to the Great Central bridge, but the sound was not at all right and the acceleration was not up to usual standards. As the train emerged from below the Northampton line bridge, it turned out to be a compound 4-4-0, sanders on, being driven just about flat out, and she had no fewer than 12 on. The fireman was digging away and everything looked as though superhuman efforts were being made. I would dearly love to know how they managed that night — but it would be a safe bet they weren't in Watford by 7.58.

The 'Patriot' design evolved, of course, from a marriage of the 'Royal Scot' chassis and the enlarged 'Claughton' boiler. The first two engines were perhaps classifiable as a rebuild of the 'Claughtons', since various components such as bogie, wheels, brake gear and reversing gear were used again. The next ten engines had new coupled wheels but were

*See *Railway Magazine*, July 1965 for a repeat of this run.

otherwise generally similar, while the remainder were almost entirely new engines with various detail differences.

Now in principle, there was nothing wrong with such a design. The 'Royal Scot' cylinders and motion, while not quite up to the most enlightened modern standards, proved satisfactory over many years of hard-driven service, and superficially the boiler and firebox were of good size for the job. Yet somehow they just did not click together as they should have done, and the result was an engine that you had to handle understandingly and humour along: hammer it you could not. There were two reasons for this. Firstly the boiler tube proportions were wrong, and secondly the draughting was deficient.

There was undoubtedly an idiosyncratic influence at work in the boiler section of the development drawing office at Derby in the late 1920s and early 1930s — it got Stanier into trouble with some of his early boilers, too. This influence led to small tubes of over-large diameter being used: in the 'Patriot' case these were $2^1/_8$in on a length between tubeplate of 14ft 0in, giving a very poor A/S ratio. So the free gas area was nearly 60% through the small tubes. Just to add to the trouble, they put $1^1/_2$in superheater elements in instead of the more normal $1^3/_8$in diameter, this obstructing the flues to the point where much of the gas was wasted through the small tubes. So it was that the only way to get a 'Patriot' along well was to let her make her own pace, on a light rein: try to flog her, and she would lay down and quickly go limp on you.

The overall draughting design of blastpipe and chimney was not a help in evening the draught out, either: it was a typical bit of Derby-Midland design, but with the chimney jammed back against the superheater header, and was reasonable with skilled enginemen and good lump coal but totally ineffective in the normal rough-and-tumble of postwar operating. The problem was recognised in the 1950s and, while no tests were done on the plants at Rugby or Swindon, a redesigned blastpipe and chimney were fitted to No 45508. The boiler remained unaltered. But by this time the writing was on the wall and by 1963 they were all gone.

In addition, there were a multitude of minor things to go wrong. The smokebox, in keeping with that of other outside-cylinder engines of Fowler origin, was rather prone to draw air at the base, particularly at high mileages when things began to 'work'. The injectors, fed from that Midland-type tender, could be very temperamental and even the vacuum pipe layout could be troublesome: there was a bit of a tangle of it adjacent to the reversing screw that leaked and fractured as soon as the engine got run down and the boiler waltzed about in the frames. So, as you can imagine, you were never remotely sure, until you were on your way, what sort of prize you had got hold of. But I'll defy anyone to get in such a mess with a 'Patriot' as Derby men used to do with No 45509.

When it was a Derby return working, *Derbyshire Yeomanry* would be stuck on the 7.55am Derby-St Pancras, to come back with the then 6.30pm St Pancras-Derby, allowed 108min to Leicester, and you could guarantee a late arrival there with No 45509. One night we rolled in about 20min down, after a pathetic exhibition of staggering up the hills and coasting down the other side, so I went up to the engine to ascertain the trouble. There was about half an inch of water visible in the gauge glasses, 150lb on the clock and the exhaust injector singing wheezily. 'The regulator's been shut since Kibworth,' the fireman said, 'the injector's been on the whole time, and this is the result. B . . . . thing!'

Probably the finest recorded work by a 'Patriot' was contained in a run published in the *Railway Magazine* in July 1933, with No 5959 (still carrying its 'Claughton' numbering) on the up 'Lancastrian' in the hands of an inspired pair from Longsight, Driver Rogers and Fireman Lennarddo. The engine had 13 coaches, 445tons gross behind the tender, a. d after being delayed by an emergency stop at Nuneaton, was worked thence to Euston, 97.1miles, in 93min. 26sec. The most spectacular section was from Bletchley to Tring. After 77½ before Wolverton, Bletchley was passed at 70½: the faintly rising grades brought this down to 65 before Cheddington, but the 6miles at 1 in 333 up to Tring were surmounted without speed falling below 61. This suggests an output in excess of 1,300 EDBHP, which was well above normal levels of contemporary work. The engine was only a few months from rebuilding, and was clearly in first-class condition.

The 'Jubilees' could hardly have been more different from the 'Patriots', once the initial teething troubles with the draughting had been put right. You did certainly meet the odd black sheep amongst them, and when you did, it could be the devil's own job to get it right — if you ever did succeed. But by and large they were a grand machine for fast running with medium-weight trains — say up to about 10 or 11 coaches — or for heavy pounding on difficult routes, or for almost anything else within their class.

Their start was certainly inauspicious, the first 113 (less five with the first tube modifications) being built with the low-superheat boiler and with a blastpipe and chimney which, designed on two or four-cylinder principles, did not suit a six-beat situation. In addition, it took time for a fireman to get used to firing a long grate with a very pronounced hump half-way along, which impeded placing coal accurately on the front half. But the low-superheat in itself did not cause steaming trouble, only heavier coal consumption, and after fitting new blastpipe caps with a 4¾in diameter orifice they steamed well enough. There was quite a lot of juggling with tube layout, diameter and numbers in small batches as construction continued, until two layouts were finalised — 24 flues and 159 1⅞in diameter tubes for tubeplate renewals, and 28 flues and 151 1⅞in diameter tubes for replacement boilers — and steaming with either layout was very satisfactory. In the meantime that odd influence at Derby had been using 2in and 2⅛in diameter tubes in combination with 14, 21, 24, and 28 elements!

What was the secret as compared with the 'Patriots'? Well, the cylinders were very similar, and nothing out of the ordinary apart from the $^5/_{16}$in lead which was eventually used on all the three-cylinder 4-6-0s. That made them very lively and strong on short cutoffs. Further, the proportions of the finalised tube layouts, allied to a firebox little smaller than that on a 'Royal Scot' and with plenty of volume to support good combustion, really got the boiler right. The result was that, provided that you could keep the water level up, a 'Jubilee' thrived on hard work, and within reason, the harder you pushed it the better it steamed. It could throw a fair bit of fire when you did push it, but that was hardly surprising.

The proviso about the water was very important, however, and it called for an exhaust steam injector that regulated as the manufacturers intended and worked cleanly over the whole range. The small 3500gallon Fowler tenders were prone to cause injector trouble due to water starvation or dirt penetration and needed very careful watching. The big Stanier tenders did not suffer to anything like the same extent in this respect.

The riding was generally very good unless very run down, and they were sweet, mechanically. In fact, very often it was possible to check speed by the sound of railjoints — and that put them in the 'Duchess' class. They usually had the feel of a big, rangy, racehorse. Just occasionally you got one a bit different — No 45717 *Dauntless* from Bank Hall was one, to the point where she was nicknamed 'Gormless', for she would wag her back end when she got into her stride, and we had to stiffen up the intermediate buffer springs on the tender to damp out these unpleasant movements.

Mechanically they caused few problems: the long, sketchily-stayed length of frame behind the intermediate coupled axle was rather whippy, and it was difficult to keep hornstays and cross-stays tight. There was also a certain amount of inside big end trouble until the circular pads were provided in the brasses: these made the fittings of 'stink bombs' in the big end journal of the crank axles unnecessary. Any attention to the inside motion, of course, was rather unpleasant, situated awkwardly as it was above the bogie centre in just about the filthiest position imaginable. One outstanding feature was the cleanliness of the piston valves at 30-36,000mile examination — so much so that it proved possible to increase the mileage to 40-48,000miles. The balanced draught of the three-cylinder engine, with little suction down the blast pipe when coasting, was the reason for this.

So by the late 1930s they were proving formidable engines indeed when driven hard in the generally good conditions prevailing. This was demonstated in overwhelming fashion in October 1937 when No 5660 *Rooke* was put through her paces with the dynamometer car on the Bristol-Leeds-Glasgow (St Enoch) route to confirm the planning of the accelerated Midland Division timetable introduced in 1938. She was certainly hammered, and produced EDBHPs in excess of 1,400 on several occasions and for up to 20min at a time. As an example, coming south from the Kilmarnock restart up to Polquhap summit, full regulator and 36% cutoff was the order of the day, allowing speeds to reach 46½ to Garrochburn, on 1 in 100, a minimum of 60 to Auchinleck, and nothing lower than 61½ on the last stage of the rise, mainly at 1 in 145/150 — all this with 305tons behind her. The climbing from Appleby to Ais Gill was no less spectacular, with the engine working on 35-40% cutoff throughout and lifting the train over the summit with no lower speed than 46½. Indeed, Ais Gill, 48.4 miles of climbing from Carlisle, was passed in the unprecedented time of 48min 36sec — 12sec over even time.

Mind you, this was no way to run a reliable service, despite the free steaming of the engine and full maintenance of pressure. On certain runs the average firing rate was 96.4lb of coal per sq ft of grate per hour, so that on the hard climbs it must have been well into three figures — killing for the fireman, and very dependent on things going right. Nevertheless, the fact was that little inferior work was being done and recorded in normal service, when the conditions warranted: *Rooke's* work was no flash-in-the-pan under dynamometer car test conditions.

And let us be under no illusions that such work was the normal order of things postwar. For instance, one of the strongholds of the 'Jubilees' was the Euston-Birmingham two-hour trains, worked mainly by Bushbury engines and shared between Bushbury and Camden men. Now these trains in the 1950s were on the LM Region's XL limit timings, on which a 'Jubilee' was allowed 350tons — say 10 bogies of BR standard stock with restaurant car — and this required even time to Coventry with a minute or two of recovery. Not untypical of these workings was a run by No 45742 *Connaught*, fitted (as were several others at various times) with a double blastpipe and chimney.

The engine was driven with the main valve of the regulator only a little open, probably giving a steam chest pressure 40-50lb sq/in below boiler pressure, and cutoffs mainly in the 15-22% range when up to speed. This was adequate to maintain slightly over 60 on the 1 in 339 to Bushey, 63 minimum over Tring, and nothing less than 64 at Kilsby Tunnel. Dowhill speeds were very moderate — only once did we exceed the low 70s — but we were into Coventry 2 min before time despite two permanent way slacks en route.

Mind you, the Bushbury men were not afraid to hammer a 'Jubilee' when the mood took them, which was more than could be said of the Camden drivers at the time, pampered as they invariably were with Pacifics and 'Royal Scots'. I was on a 'Scot' backing down to Euston to work either the 2.30pm Liverpool or 2.40pm Manchester one afternoon, and we were held just by the down side carriage shed for the 2.20pm Birmingham coming out. The Bushbury men were laying into Camden bank with a vengeance — straight column of smoke and steam and plenty of noise from the 'Jubilee's' chimney. The Camden driver looked on with an air of distaste, and finally could not contain himself any longer. 'Just look at those silly b . . . . . . s going about it like that!'. Camden men were a bit that way!

I also recall a trip on one of these trains in the up direction, when inadvertently I made myself very unpopular with the enginemen. We had one of the engines with the big Stanier 3,500gallon tenders — the ones that look like a 4,000gallon tender only were slightly shorter. Now those tenders had a water gauge identical to that of their big sisters, but it was only calibrated up to 3,500 and you had to look closely to see that the '4,000' figure was not there. I didn't!

The fireman was getting a bite to eat as we approached Lawford troughs, so I operated the scoop for him, and as the pointer got up to 3,500 I was musing 'another 200gallons and I'll start getting the scoop out,' when we were deluged on the footplate by coal-dirty water from the tank vents in the bunker and a fountain of water up the gauge hole. The wind caught the water as it flowed over the edge of the footplate and blew it back as spray all over us. It took us until Weedon to get dry.

When it came to hill-climbing, I confess that I was in something of a quandary. All my instincts told me that the crisp bark of a Class 5 was more attuned to the need of the Midland route to Carlisle than the throaty roar of a 'Jubilee', but often doubts crept in after you had seen 'Jubilees' on such hard climbing jobs. You had only to hear the distant sounds that floated up to the Derbyshire hills as a down Manchester express opened up from the 45mph slack on Rowsley curve: there was none of the jazzy beat of a Gresley engine, but a lovely even purr that told of a front end in good fettle. And a 'Jubilee' could chop her beats off short and sharp when she was nicely warmed up.

Let me tell a tale of a trip from Edinburgh in the early 1950s on the 'Thames-Forth Express'. We had an A3 Pacific, *Bayardo*, from Waverley to Carlisle with 10 LMS bogies including diner, 317 tons, and a more pathetic exhibition would be hard to find than the work done on that stage (the A3s were hopeless for slogging up the steep gradients of the Waverley route until they got their double chimneys). The engine had about as much life in it as the horse after which it was named has now, and we staggered up to Falahill and Whitrope with the pressure gauge needle and the water gauge vying with each other for the lowest position. With such a moderate load for a Pacific (the permitted load was 350 tons) and unchecked we rolled into Carlisle nearly 10min late; here the A3 was replaced by a singularly grimy Holbeck 5X, No 45619, with one of those slab-sided 3,500gallon tenders loaded with some dubious-looking coal. My heart sank — and did not rise again until we were a couple of miles on our way (having left Carlisle 7 min late). At this juncture the driver, a Hellifield man, casually announced that he wanted to get 'several minutes in hand' before Appleby so that he could fill his little tender up. From the way he said it, it was obvious that he had complete confidence in the engine's ability to do it.

The running was not quite up to *Rooke* standards, but good none-the-less. We were into Appleby 4½ min net under schedule, with the engine worked with full regulator and mainly 20-25% on the screw. From the restart, we passed Ais Gill summit, 17.6miles, in only 28sec over the allowance of 29min, despite two pw slacks, one before Grisburn and the other to 15 before Crosby Garrett. From these, 35-32% cutoff was the order of the day, and we cleared Ais Gill at no lower than 33mph having been up to 43 at Smardale viaduct and 41 on the easy stretch past Mallerstang. Boiler pressure was ready to lift the safety valves, water well up in the glass, and there was a distinctly satisfied look in the eyes of driver and fireman.

With the sort of record I have outlined, it was somewhat surprising that in 1955 the headquarters operators should have asked that the 'Jubilees' be put through stationary plant tests to make their steaming reliable. Nevertheless, the result was that 45722 went to the Rugby plant in 1956. The report on these tests was never published, but it established a front end limit of evaporation for this engine of just under 21,000lb/hr, which was markedly inferior to that of a Class 5. A fancy blastpipe with sharp-edged orifice, and slightly smaller chimney, was developed, and this was steamed up to 24,500lb/hr. A similar double blastpipe and chimney were also tested pushing the limit up to 26,000lb/hr, all these on Grade 2B Blidworth coal. These experimental blastpipes, together with the standard arangement, are shown in Fig 3. Everyone preened themselves at the thought of the improvement effected.

But was it real? First of all, there were plenty of recorded cases of standard 'Jubilees' being steamed at rates well over 21,000lb/hr for very long periods, and this is not consistent with the front end limit that Rugby established. It looks as though No 45722 was a rather poor specimen at the start. Furthermore, when the re-draughted single chimney engines were put into traffic, they were certainly no improvement on the standard ones. I had No 45702 at Newton Heath, and on the Glasgow workings from Manchester her steaming offered no more reserve, and as boiler washout neared it deteriorated noticeably. This was due to carbon build-up in the orifice, to which this sharp-edged design was extremely sensitive; it had to be carefully cleaned at every fortnightly washout, and preferably at each 'boiler full' examination intermediately. It was a great disappointment: how much better, to provide a margin for poorer coals, to have put on the plain double chimney *à la* No 45742.

This was the only attempt to adapt the 'Jubilees', an excellent, proved design, to the hard, post-war world of declining coal standards (mainly in size rather than quality), curtailed fireman experience, and more difficult servicing and maintenance conditions. It was not effective, and it was made too late, for the diesels were already on order.

But even after this time, and with the writing becoming increasingly clear on the wall, the 'Jubilees' were putting up some first-rate — even

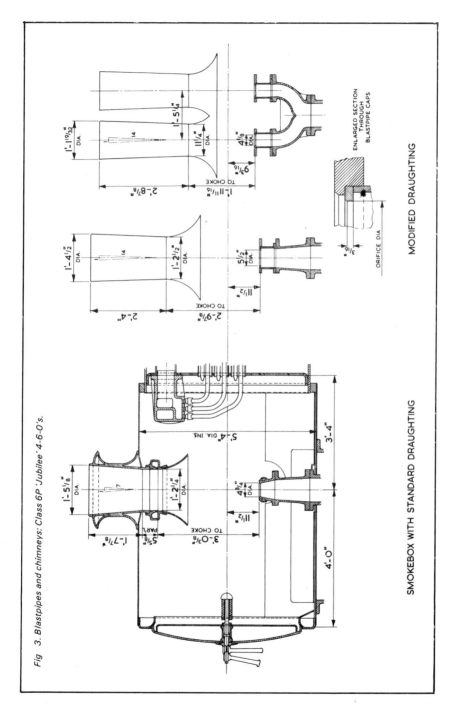

Fig. 3. Blastpipes and chimneys: Class 6P 'Jubilee' 4-6-0's.

ENLARGED SECTION THROUGH BLASTPIPE CAPS

MODIFIED DRAUGHTING

SMOKEBOX WITH STANDARD DRAUGHTING

63

superlative — performances. One classic involved No 45593 *Kolhapur* on the 4.15pm Carlisle-Preston semifast,* not quite the sort of job to expect fireworks on. But with a nine-coach train of 307 tons tare and well loaded, *Kolhapur* accelerated from the Penrith stop to 49mph at Eden Valley Junction and was driven hard enough to sustain a minimum of 39½mph on the long, telling 1 in 125 to Harrison's Sidings. The slight easing of gradient and short level past Shap station raised this to 48, and the Summit was cleared at a minimum of 43. My calculations suggest an EDBHP of about 1,650 on the climb, and this was sustained for about 20min. The 'Jubilee' spirit was clearly undimmed when called upon.

*See *Railway Magazine*, January 1963.

9/High Born Ladies

In Chapter 1, I touched on the appearance in June 1933 of the first of Mr Stanier's 'Princesses', No 6200. Looking back to earlier days at Rugby, when Pacifics were just something one read about on the LNER — the A1s had yet to appear on the Great Central Section — and the biggest passenger engines on the LMS were the 'Royal Scots' (massive-looking engines, to be sure, particularly in their parallel-boiler form) one realises how rapidly the size of LMS locomotives increased during the 1930s, even though the numbers were very small. *Princess Royal's* 74ft of engine and tender, weighing almost 157tons, was a sizeable step up from the 63ft and 128tons of the 'Royal Scots'.

Pacific 'firsts' until the 1930s do not seem to have been outstandingly successful. *The Great Bear* was not really superior to a 'Star', and was cut down to a 4-6-0 with few regrets. The Raven Pacifics were a thorough flop, with a poor front end and a most misproportioned boiler: even rebuilding with an A1 boiler could not save them from the inevitable. Only the Gresley Pacifics survived, and they needed the fitting of long-lap valves and motion before they came into their own. The 'Princesses' did quite a lot to break that sequence, once they got proper combustion chamber boilers and a reasonable degree of superheat. Even so, the early promise of their performance in the late 1930s seldom came through into the 1950s. Rather like the 'Patriots', they were overshadowed and out-performed by the machines that followed them, and while they were not allowed to go to the wall as the 'Patriots' generally were, they were never used on the hardest jobs and crews were mentally dropping time before they ever climbed aboard.

But what work they put up in the 1936-39 period! Firstly their large grate enabled them to work right through between Euston and Glasgow, and their capabilities encouraged the operating department to timetable some very fast running with heavy trains. I suppose the trains that the 'Princesses' will always be associated with during that era were the 'Midday Scot' and the 5.25pm Liverpool-Euston.

The 'Midday' was no mean task from 1936, especially for a through engine working. It was allowed 163min to Crewe (158.1miles) which was not difficult. The following 79min to Lancaster (71.9miles) was appropriate for the then state of the road between Wigan and Preston, which was never free from subsidence slacks. But then it had to pull its finger out, for 59min were allowed to the Penrith stop, 51.2miles including the climbs to Grayrigg and Shap Summit. Then with reduced load from Carlisle with the hiving off of the Edinburgh section, it had to be in Glasgow Central in 116min (102.1 miles over Beattock), by which time the fire was getting dirty and the coal was way back in the tender. Speaking of this train in the *Railway Magazine* of December 1936, the late Cecil J. Allen said:

'...the LMS Pacifics become a little uncertain in their performance when the loads near the 600ton mark and timekeeping, as yet, proves to be a matter of some difficulty with 17coach and 18coach trains . . .'

Ye gods! I'm not surprised. Certainly, his tabulations showed the odd minute or two being habitually dropped on that gruelling timing from the Lancaster start to Shap Summit with more than 500tons gross, and sometimes with less. But try this for size*

No 6208 had a 16coach train of 515tons gross, which she brought into Penrith in 56minutes 10sec: 71mph at Carnforth, nothing less than 55½ over Yealand hump, 67½ at Milnthorpe, 45 at Lambrigg, 42¼ minimum at Grayrigg on the two miles of 1 in 106, 66½ before Tebay, and a minimum of 28½ at Shap Summit, passed in 43½ minutes. 'Some difficulty', yes — but what a magnificent show.

It was not just a capability for heavy haulage that marked the 'Princesses' either; they could run, and run fast. These qualities were never better demonstrated than during the high-speed test runs in November 1936 from Euston to Glasgow and back, with 6hr timings each way. *Princess Elizabeth,* in the expert hands of a pair of Crewe North enginemen, Driver Tom Clarke and Fireman C. Fleet, and with a seven-coach train of 230tons including dynamometer car, cut the timings by 7min in the down direction and by no less than 15¼min on the up run. Going north 90mph was reached or exceeded on seven separate occasions, with a maximum of 95½, while southbound, the same speed was reached four times, with a maximum of 95† on the level at Coppenhall Junction. The dynamometer car test report said that 'the steaming of the engine was completely satisfactory ...practically full boiler pressure being maintained throughout'. (At the time No 6201 carried a hybrid boiler, with 32 superheater elements but the original firebox, without combustion chamber, thus giving 20ft-9in long tubes). Coal consumption was 46.8 and 44.8lb/mile on the two runs: these figures were not greatly different from those taken a month previously with No 6210 on the 'Royal Scot' with loads between 482 and 552tons south of Symington.

---

*See *Railway Magazine,* September 1936.
†The dynamometer car test report gives fractionally lower speeds.

Well, that's what they *could* do. But very often they fell very short of such standards. There were usually several allocated to Edge Hill postwar, and there the maintenance staff seemed able to keep them in better condition than at Camden, Crewe North or Upperby. The Edge Hill top link men managed to get more out of the 'Lizzies' than any other: they seemed to have a certain feel for them, and that was more essential with a 'Princess' than a 'Duchess'. With the latter there was scope for some free-and-easy handling, and the engine would still steam freely. But not with a 'Princess'. You'd got to be much more precise, keeping the fire at the right, tapering thickness, with back corners well filled and appropriate damper settings. Get it wrong, and the pressure gauge needle would be hanging back. Ease up on the injector, let the water level get down a bit, and if the fire was not right and the pressure did not respond in lively fashion, you were soon struggling. Why was this? Well, I think there were two reasons, leaving aside any defect such as leaking superheater elements, the smokebox drawing air, or the like which would adversely affect steaming. The first was the boiler proportions: the second the single chimney draughting.

As to the boiler proportions, one thing was crystal clear: for the size of the firebox, the boiler barrel was too small, and probably too long, even with the combustion chamber. Within the limitations of the firebox tubeplate, the tube layout with 32 superheater flues could give no greater free gas area than 5.97sq ft, or 13.2% of grate area. Not only that, but the tube proportions were not good, particularly the superheater flues, which were sufficiently constricting to limit the gas flow through them, and hence the superheat temperature: this seldom reached 650°F, even when working hard. Undoubtedly the use of $5\frac{1}{2}$in flues, as on the BR standard wide-firebox boilers, would have been beneficial, but only an increase in barrel diameter would have been the real answer—as was done on the 'Duchesses': the extra $2\frac{1}{2}$in of diameter at the firebox end permitted another 0.92 sq ft of free gas area.

Then there was the single chimney. Whether it was capable of improvement I do not know, because I do not think anyone tried, but it is significant that the single chimney on the early 'Duchesses' was something of a let-down when they had to be pushed hard, as the first — unpublicised — test run with *Duchess of Abercorn* showed in February 1939. It is all too probable that a double chimney on the 'Princesses' would have brought about a considerable improvement in steaming reliability.

Then there were mechanical weaknesses which undoubtedly lowered availability and reacted on reliability and steaming. First of all the outside cylinders, located over the trailing bogie wheels, gave a lot of trouble with loosening. The plain fact was that, because of the inside motion, the frames could have very little horizontal staying in this zone — there was only the bogie centre in front and the exhaust breeches pipe between the cylinders, the rest being simple vertical stretchers, and so a lot of racking of the frames could take place, destroying the tightness of the cylinder bolts. As soon as this happened the movement transferred itself to the exhaust channels, which loosened and often fractured — and this usually impacted on the steaming by leaking exhaust steam into the smokebox. As so often in locomotive design, the layout in this area was necessarily a compromise: one either put in a massive structure which produced a robust frame but made access to the inside motion appalling for preparation and maintenance (as on the GWR four-cylinder locomotives) or left it reasonably open for human access and suffered some flexing.

In the end, when normal shop repairs were ineffective, the decision was taken to support the cylinder bolts by welding buttress strips on to the frame plates fore and aft of the outside cylinder flanges, with fitted packings between, and this was fairly successful. Crewe applied this arrangement by keeping a spare front end frame section, complete with cylinders and stretchers and extending back to the leading coupled axle horns; when a 'Princess' came in for general repair, the front of the old frames was cut off and the replacement unit welded on.

The original regulators, in the superheater header in the smokebox, were distinctly 'heavy' to handle, and lacked sensitivity (a serious design weakness on an engine with a lot of power in relation to its adhesion.) In fact, I used to watch little Laurie Earl of Camden on occasion — he was about as tall as six penny-worth of coppers — when he got the 'rightaway' at Rugby, run across the cab and positively launch himself at the regulator handle. In addition, there was a fairly heavy mortality of headers themselves, due to fractures — and that didn't do the steaming much good, either! So all the 'Princess' boilers were converted to dome regulators in the early 1950s. To pile on the agony, there was some trouble with fracturing of the rear bissel truck frames and loose rivet attachments to the radial arm — an occurrence also not unknown on the 'Duchesses' with the similar arrangement. And even the coupled wheel centres seemed to come from a poor batch of castings — the Crewe Steel Foundry was notorious for the porosity and sand inclusions in its products — and spoke fractures were not infrequent.

Undoubtedly, some of these weaknesses (and particularly the inadequacy of the boiler) were coming to light when the need for further 'Pacifics' for the new high-speed Euston-Glasgow service in 1937 was established. Despite the brave note struck in the dynamometer car report on the 'Princess Elizabeth' high speed trial—'a six-hour schedule . . . is quite practicable, and is within the capacity, without undue stress, of the Class 7 4-6-2 passenger engine' — it was well that the HQ people at Derby appreciated the need for a better machine to run the 'Coronation Scot' service, day in and day out, with enginemen of different skills, variable coal, and a reserve of power to recover from delays, if that service was to show proper reliability. Mr Stanier had to produce a bigger boiler and then adapt the 'Princess' chassis to carry it.

Bigger grate, bigger firebox volume, bigger free gas area, bigger barrel, bigger superheater — all these were incorporated in that delightful boiler. It was pushed upward so that the front corners of the Belpaire firebox were up to the limit of the loading gauge, just enabling 6ft 9in wheels to be accommodated underneath it. (Incidentally, what was it that was so magical about 6ft 9in diameter coupled wheels for express passenger engines in this country?). The cylinder layout was altered back to a conventional one, but retaining the divided drive, thus enabling rocking levers to be fitted behind the cylinders and avoiding valve setting troubles due to thermal expansion. It enabled the steam and exhaust passages to be better steamlined internally, and the crew's access for preparation between the frames to be made more congenial. The result — the 'Duchesses', and under that generic title I lump together the whole 38 engines from 46220 to 46257. Apart from incidental modifications such as rocking grates, roller bearings and the like, they were all essentially the same.

Initially the 'Duchesses' went into service on the streamlined Euston-Glasgow trains, which they handled with complete ease: power outputs of 1250 EDBHP or so were fully adequate to work these trains to time south of Carlisle, though in Scotland the work demanded was rather harder. The pre-service trial run for the press on 29 June 1937 produced some very fast running, including a brief record speed of 113mph down Madeley bank and a remarkable 119min run from Crewe to Euston: it also came near to producing disaster headlines, for in the anxiety to get a record down Madeley bank, the braking for Crewe was left too late. The train hit the reverse curves at Crewe South Junction, limited to 20mph at 52: only by great good fortune was the train not derailed, for the track was damaged by the side thrusts. A major 'hushup' job was done, and the incident was not publicised until 10½ years later.

But the 'Duchesses' were going to have to earn their keep by fast haulage of heavy trains, not by working light trains at high speeds. The operating authorities at Euston, noting that the 'Princesses' were not fully on top of the 7hr timings to Glasgow with the heaviest trains, wanted to see whether their new machines could work even heavier trains reliably on such timings. In February 1939, therefore, No 6234 *Duchess of Abercorn* ran tests between Crewe and Glasgow on the 7hr timings with a train of 604 tons tare. The first tests were made in her standard (at that time) single chimney form; and the results received no publicity — understandably, for overall performance fell some way short of expectations. Steaming under hard condtions was not reliable and point-to-point times could not be kept; pressure was down in the 200-220lb/sq in range on the major climbs. From Carlisle to Beattock, thanks to low boiler pressure and some mismanagement of the fire by the Polmadie crew who took over at Carlisle, nearly 9½min were dropped. Clearly this was not going to be practical for regular operating, and so the engine was put into Crewe Works to be fitted with a double blastpipe and chimney of straightforward design. The tests were then repeated two weeks later.

The difference in the results was truly remarkable, for now steaming was all that could be desired, even at very extended rates of working. Cutoffs on the northbound climbs were up to 25% on Grayrigg, 35% on Shap, and 40% on the last stages of Beattock, the minimum speeds with this great train being 41, 30 and 30mph respectively. But on the return, the performance was even more impressive: 30-35% cutoff up to Craigenhill summit sustained 43-44mph, with DBHP (not corrected for engine weight) about 2,000; similarly to Beattock summit, passed at 63 (2,282 DBHP), which must have required steaming at about 39,000lb/hr. Even more spectacular was the climb from Carlisle to Shap Summit: 30-35% cutoff to Calthwaite, at 64mph (2,511 DBHP) and up to 40% to Shap Summit, breasted at 38mph (2,331 DBHP max). These were quite new standards for the West Coast main line, but gruelling for the fireman, for he was shifting something over 2 tons/hr. Overall coal consumption was heavy at 68.7lb/mile, but efficiency was good in relation to work — 3.12lb/DBHP/h. No wonder the double chimney was quickly standardised!*

What can one say of the 'Duchesses' in service? They were superb riding engines, steady, entirely free from nosing or back end 'wag', giving a degree of comfort, even at high mileages, little inferior to that of a carriage. The excellent steaming of the 6234 trial was carried forward into the whole class, and in relation to the work done they were highly economical. Mind you, one had really got to build up the fire before one started: two tons in the firebox was about the minimum to come off the shed with, and that needed adding to before any real work was done. The important thing was to get the back corners well filled and heaped up.

I often wondered why British designs of wide fireboxes made the back end of the grate so wide. It was bad enough on a 'Princess' at about 5ft-6in, but with the 'Duchess' grate, having the same overall length of firebox and 5 more square feet to get in, this was increased to about 6ft-2in. That meant that at each side of the firehole there was about 2ft-3in of grate which had to be kept filled by a combination of wrist action on the shovel and a certain amount of prodding — all done with at least one hand almost in the firehole. It was hardly surprising that firemen invariably wore a glove on their forward hand when working a 'Duchess', even if they used one on no other engine. The fireman's lot could have been eased considerably if a more trapezoidal grate, tapering to about 5ft wide, had been provided, even at the expense of a few inches on the length. After all, with a thick fire at the back, the front of the grate would feed itself with only an occasional shovelful to keep things even.

Slipping was a thing to be guarded against — and these big engines,

*For more detailed results of this trial, see the author's contribution to *The LMS Duchesses,* Ed. D. Doherty. MAP 1973.

with a lot of power in relation to the adhesion weight, required especial care. The use of independently sprung axleboxes, without equalisation to give an effective three-point suspension of the locomotive, gave rise to a degree of weight transfer on curvature and through points and crossings which could lighten the adhesion weight available. And once you did start to really slip, it could be extremely destructive if not checked very rapidly. That was not easy, because of the enormous volume of steam between the dome regulator and the pistons. The combination of large steam pipes (7in dia. main, 6in from the header), 40-element superheater, and roomy steam chests meant that, after the regulator was shut, there was still enough 'uncontrolled' steam beyond it to turn the wheels 1½ times at full cutoff and boiler pressure. This, combined with the reduction in wheel-rail friction as soon as slipping commenced, could lead to a 'raceaway' slip before the driver reacted and took preventive action. Heaven help him in trying to close the regulator if she picked up water with the steam from over-filling of the boiler! Some drivers were in the habit of opening and closing the regulator several times quickly, as a sort of crude throttling technique. What it really needed, of course, was a multiple valve regulator on the superheat side of the header — something from which British CMEs shied away.

Preparation was less arduous than on a 'Princess', for there were fewer oiling points and less clambering about between the frames: there was access to all the inside motion, except the big ends, from the access holes in front of the outside cylinders, if the engine was set properly.

Just after the war, with shed staff at a low ebb in numbers and supervision, when the rocking grate, hopper ashpan and selfcleaning smokebox seemed to offer great advantages, a number of 'Duchesses' so equipped ran into trouble with partial collapse of the rocking grate, particularly at the sides and front corners. After days of examination over the ashpits at Camden and Crewe North, and in fire-boxes and ashpans, the trouble was identified as a build-up of ash and clinker on the sloping surfaces of the pan, aided and abetted by dribbles from a sluicing system which was also fitted in the ashpan sides. With the rear-end frame construction used on these engines, this defect was inherent, due to the inability to make the ashpan sides slope sufficiently to be self-cleaning. As a palliative, access doors were fitted at the front corners of the ashpans to enable the danger spots to be raked down, but the back end of the last two engines was completely redesigned, using a single slab frame each side and a new ashpan with full-length side access doors.

In terms of train performance, it is perhaps not unfair to say that the 'Duchesses' did not really come into their own until the early 1950s, when 'XL, Limit' timings started to reappear, in some cases with very heavy trains. They had already given a good idea of their extraordinary capabilities when No 46225 was put through her paces on the Rugby Test Plant and on the road in 1957.

My own personal *pièce de resistance* with one was recorded on the

Friday before Whitsun, 1953, on the down 'Mid-day Scot'. No 46255 *City of Hereford* came on to a train of 16 bogies at Crewe. There had been a relief train ahead, hauled by a 'Royal Scot', which had left after the 4.24pm departure time of the regular train and when we got the 'rightaway' we were no less than 17min late. The Crewe North driver — whose name I have regrettably mislaid — decided to play along gently and see how how the relief was running before setting about the recovery of the arrears, and his wisdom soon became apparent when signals at Acton Grange Junction and Golborne Junction brought us down to 25 and 15mph. We rolled through Preston, having just kept sectional time, only to be checked again just beyond. We then crawled away to Garstang, sighting distants that cleared as we approached them, and there, when things appeared more clear, got moving normally again, only to be pulled down to walking pace approaching Carnforth; for a Manchester-Windermere train had been sandwiched between the relief train and ourselves. There was an easy recovery from this check, but then we ran into another at Oxenholme, where we eased through the platform up to the starter, no less than 33min late, at a speed that a driver walking to sign off could have bettered.

Then we got the road with Grayrigg ahead from almost a standing start. Up went the regulator handle to the full-open stop, the reversing gear was set to 28 per cent, and with 225lb on the clock *City of Hereford* heaved her long train into the curves of Grayrigg bank with a sharp and exultant bark. (She was blowing off at 235lb, unfortunately.) She was not pushed unduly up the bank, in view of what had gone before, but speed was worked up to 36 and sustained there on the 1 in 106 to Grayrigg station. Once over the top, acceleration was rapid and we swept over Dillicar troughs, picking up 1,750 gallons in the process, at 68mph.

Now, with the fells looming in the front cab windows, our driver showed his enginemanship to the full. No fall in speed took place before he was 'dropping her down'; as we ran up to Tebay station the cut-off was put to 25 per cent, and then down by successive stages until, as we went by Scout Green at 49mph *City of Hereford* was talking to the tune of 35 per cent. The box was barely past when she was put down to 40 per cent, and then to 50 per cent. The Westmorland sheep scurried away at the din, hardened creatures though they were! Pressure was dropping slightly, but the water level was being well held, and we were all set to clear the top unaltered, when she slipped.

The driver was waiting for just that and the regulator was quickly shut: when the slip stopped, he dropped her down to 60 per cent and opened the regulator — gingerly at first, then further as she held her feet, and finally up to the full-open position again. For the last quarter-mile up to the summit, as a final gesture of defiance, the driver dropped her down into full gear. *City of Hereford* had got the lot and was keeping her feet! We blasted our way past Shap Summit box at 31mph, in a deafening noise that rattled the signalbox windows, having almost kept sectional time from Oxenholme, despite the crawling start. A smart run down to Carlisle brought us in just under 32 minutes late.

The station staff at Carlisle took no less than 10½min to detach two rear coaches and get us ready to depart again, instead of the 7min allowed (was it ever different? not in my experience!) and then with tank replenished we started the real business of time recovery. Full regulator and cut-offs between 20 and 25 per cent were used, and we began to see what a 'Duchess' could do when opened out. After 75 over Floriston troughs (which were empty, under repair) we kept up a speed between 63 and 77 over this undulating but generally rising road, and romped into Beattock station, 39.7 miles, in exactly 37½min, for 800gallons of water. We had used 1,700gallons from Carlisle, a fairly high figure at 42.8gallons per mile, but *City of Hereford* had certainly been giving value for money.

After a considerable delay a Caledonian 0-4-4 tank buffered up to our tail, but I do not think he was quite prepared for the speeds he was expected to match. We started off easily, with full regulator and 25% cutoff, then lengthened to 35 and finally to 40%. As we slogged up Beattock between the pinewoods, the traffic on the A74 road alongside overtook us for a while; then as the beat quickened we began to overtake things ourselves, until by Greskine Siding we were up to 43mph (on 1 in 74!). Unfortunately we had to slack to 15mph for a bridge renewal slowing at Harthope viaduct, but we recovered from this to 36 by the Summit, passed in 18min. 21sec against the pass-to-pass allowance of 20min. Restrained downhill running brought us into Carstairs in 43min 7sec from Beattock and 86min 5sec from Carlisle, or almost exactly as booked, in spite of almost 5½min standing at Beattock, the permanent way slack at Harthope and another at Abington, and signals approaching Carstairs. Net running time from Carlisle I estimate at 74min or almost exactly a mile a minute.

No 46225 *Duchess of Gloucester* was on the Rugby plant, and on confirmatory tests over the Settle & Carlisle line, during 1957/8: the results were never made available to the public in an official test bulletin. One can only say, having read the internal test report, that the performance was immensely impressive. She was steamed at rates up to 41,500lb/hr, and at this output the limit of the boiler or front end were not really in sight; it was merely 'appreciably above' this figure. No locomotive in this country had ever produced such continuous power. What limited the output was, in the first place, adhesion (there was a fair amount of slipping trouble, on the plant and on the road) and, on the road, the sheer difficulty of handling bagged coal at the tender shovelling plate at a rate close on 3 tons/hr. But in spite of all this, what a magnificent performance she gave! Alas, it was too late to have any effect on operations; within two-three years the 'Duchesses' were bumped on to secondary work and by the end of 1964 all had been withdrawn.

Looking at the published records of 'Duchess' performance in day-to-day service in the 1950s, when they really came into their own, it is very noticeable how Edge Hill and Crewe North men were involved in the really outstanding runs. The former — what a great top link it was at Edge Hill at the time — worked one of the toughest jobs on the LM Region, the 7.55am combined Euston to Liverpool & Manchester train, which divided at Crewe. It called at Watford to pick up, and was booked non-stop to Crewe, 140.7 miles, in the 'XL Limit' timing of 136min. This train regularly loaded to 16 bogies, sometimes to 17 (the load limit for a 'Duchess' on these timings was 510 tons tare) and was required to be through Rugby in the level hour.

As a fine example of Edge Hill work,* No 46229 with 16 coaches on this train, totalling 535 tons gross, and in the hands of Driver Aitchison and Fireman Corfield, worked up from the Watford start to a steady 64 on the climb to Tring. That would involve about 25% cutoff and a steam rate of some 32,000lb/hr for 1800 EDBHP. There were no high speeds, but three permanent way slacks did not prevent the train being through Stafford right time. Then a ferocious attack on the climb to Whitmore was made, at about 30% cutoff, and speed rose from the 54 at which Stafford was passed to no less than 74½ at the top. What gorgeous sounds must have been wafted over the North Staffordshire countryside in the process of producing the just over 2200 EDBHP involved! The net time from Watford to Crewe was no more than 125 min.

Lest Crewe North men should feel out-shone, however, one final run† may be quoted which, in some respects, was perhaps marginally finer still. No 46224 was the engine, loaded to 525tons tare and 570tons gross on the down 'Midday Scot', and the engine was most skilfully handled by Driver Nicklin and Fireman Roberts. The minimum speed on the steady climb to Tring was 63mph, but better was to follow. After a slowing approaching Bletchley, speed was worked up to 72 beyond Wolverton and held at this level all the way over the Roade hump on 1 in 330, which needed rather more than 2,300 EDBHP. But the engine was in no way wearied by this, because on little better than level road she then accelerated to a glorious 88 at Weedon. For close on 20min Fireman Clarke must have been firing almost continuously, for this tremendous power required about a ton of coal in that period, although with Weedon behind him he could ease off somewhat and run the boiler down a little in readiness for the Rugby stop. From the restart, even time was achieved by Atherstone, and rather less spectacular running was well adequate for meticulous timekeeping, despite another permanent way slack near Madeley.

I think I have said enough about these magnificent engines to show that they were almost in a class of their own. They were held in profound

*See *Railway Magazine,* July 1955.
†See *Trains Illustrated,* January 1959.

74

respect by enginemen, and with good reason. But their full potential was never realised in traffic, for it depended, in the last analysis, on the physical effort of the fireman. They never quite succeeded, either, in the operating attempt to get 100,000miles a year from them, for a variety of reasons, many of which involved random and relatively trivial defects. Here was a real case for fitting with mechanical stokers, and making various modifications to improve mechanical endurance. What a great pity it was never done.

10/The Strong Pull

The three major constituent companies of the LMS in England and Wales — the LNWR, the Midland and the L&Y — each had their own ideas about how to move freight, coloured by the nature of the traffic, the characteristics of the road over which it was hauled, and the personalities of the responsible senior officers of the line. The LNWR, predominantly on easy grades, though with such tough sections as the Central Wales line and the route to Leeds, pinned its faith to eight-coupled wheels for the majority of its freight work, which was of a varied nature, and moved it about in long and heavy trains. The 'Lanky', dealing to a rather greater extent with mineral traffic on a moderately graded line over the Pennines, likewise used eight-coupled wheels on its 'Teddy-Bears'. On the other hand the Midland, which was a predominantly mineral line with the long haul to London and the West of England over a far-from-easy road, could produce nothing bigger than a moderate-sized 0-6-0 for the job, and double-headed anything with a respectable load behind it.

Such was the position inherited in 1923: the Midland operating influence thereafter for some years was so strong, in the person of Anderson, the Motive Power Superintendent, that what was regarded as suitable sauce for the Midland goose was insisted on for the other constituents' gander, whether or not it was palatable. More and more Class 4F's were churned out for several years until the Operating Dept. finally decided that something with more sheer guts was required, particularly for the Midland Division. The results — and I suspect that both must have gone very much against the grain at Derby — were the first three Garratts and the Class 7F 0-8-0s, otherwise known as 'Austin Sevens'.

The Garratts were really dreadful engines and went to the scrap heap unsung, unloved and in no way mourned. They proved themselves, for all practical purposes, unmaintainable — they needed to be shopped at appallingly low mileages, latterly of the order of 20-25,000miles — and did nothing significant that a 2-8-0 could not do.

Now let me emphasise that there is nothing whatever wrong with the Beyer-Garratt principle; it has been (and continues to be, in some countries) proved as a sound concept of great capability and Beyer, Peacock's reputation as designers and builders of fine engines has never been challenged. I have no doubt at all that if the LMS had given the Gorton Foundry an operating specification for what they wanted a machine to do, and then left Gorton to get on with the design and construction, the result would have been a machine that all could have been proud of. Instead the LMS got what it deserved for interfering, Nos 4997-9 and their 30 later sisters. How Beyer, Peacock's must have smiled inwardly. Furthermore, it has been revealed by E. S. Cox* that all the early negotiations with Beyer, Peacock were carried out by Anderson, as the Motive Power chief, without involving the CME until a late stage.

There was insistance on a thoroughly Midland design. The coupled wheelbase was to be the time-hallowed Derby 8ft 0in plus 8ft 6in. As much of the detail as possible was to be the same as the Midland's biggest freight engine, the Class 4F 0-6-0, and where, as with the outside cylinders and motion, this was not appropriate, the model to be followed was the Somerset and Dorset 2-8-0. One could be excused for thinking that Derby had a death-wish on the result, that they *wanted* them to be a failure on account of some 'I told you so' urge. So they emerged — and remained throughout their rather painful existence — with undersized axleboxes, the usual Midland non-adjustable spring gear, an indifferent cylinder design and an almost prehistoric Walschaerts valve gear layout giving a travel of 3¾ in, little more than half what was even then coming to be considered as normal. To listen to a Garratt was rather depressing — nothing but a sense of indistinct, deep-throated wuffles almost impossible to identify as the normal discrete beats of a conventional steam locomotive. One feature was quite noticeable, and provoked a lot of learned correspondence in the engineering journals about its causes: this was the way in which the two independent engines seemed quickly to synchronise when working.

There was usually a fair amount of stream leakage from the pipe connections at the pivot centres — Beyer Peacock self-adjusting pivot centres came along rather later, and were never fitted to the LMS Garratts — and also from the steam engine driving the rotary bunker, which spent an out-of-sight, out-of-mind existence wreathed in wet coal slurry and other filth behind the cab. There were occasions, notably in winter, when this was so bad as to cause the driver to fail the engine — they just had no proper visibility for signals.

Another weakness of the Garratts was brake power, which did nothing to endear them to drivers who were working unfitted coal trains over the lengthy gradients of the Midland line south of the Toton yards. There was no shortage of adhesion weight when everything was full, but it varied so much as the water and coal were used up — about 12tons reduction on each engine in the extreme — that the brake power had to be tailored down to the light condition, and as a result was actually less than on a Class 8 2-8-0. Not only that, but the lengthy steam pipe runs to

*Locomotive Panorama, Volume 1 Ian Allan 1965.

the brake cylinders, particularly that on the leading engine, needed a certain amount of warming up before the brake became fully effective.

Of course the basic concept of using Garratts was not properly thought through in the first place. Here was a locomotive which was to eliminate double-heading with two 0-6-0s on the Toton-Brent coal trains: it succeeded, but so could — and subsequently did — a 2-8-0. One really wonders why, in 1926/7 when the decision was taken — and after trials on the Midland with a Somerset & Dorset 2-8-0 — that solution was not adopted. It would have been much cheaper, lighter on the track (even with the big G9BS boiler the S&D engines had no axleload over 16tons, as compared with 21tons on the Garratts), and their brake power was indisputable. Not only that, but the fireman would not have been made the scapegoat that he was, having to fire 44sq ft of grate which had, in double-headed days, been done by two men.

Shovelling rather more than a hundredweight of coal per mile, the fireman lived no life of slippered ease. The cab, fully enclosed, could get stiflingly hot in summer, and before the days of the revolving coal bunkers this must have been compounded by two other 'pleasures' for the fireman — a filthy coal-dust-laden draught through the bunker when running bunker-first, and a certain amount of hiking back into the bunker on the later stages of a through run to get at the coal. If ever a design demanded either a mechanical stoker or oil firing to enable it to develop its theoretical capability, this was it; it was normal practice with the larger Garratts abroad, unless two firemen were carried. As it was, the LMS bought, at their own insistence, machines whose running costs, in relation to the work done, were as sky-high as their exhausts when working hard.

Whatever confidence may have existed in the use of Garratts on the Midland for *their* freight problem, it was clear that it was not a universal panacea, and in 1929 massive orders for a new 0-8-0 tender engine began to materialise. Derby had taken the LNWR G2 design, which was sound in overall layout if deficient in some details, and slightly modified the boiler into a Midland standard mould — designated the G7¾S — 'modernised' the frames, cylinders and motion, put a Fowler 3500gallon tender behind it, and proudly exhibited it as the last word in freight locomotives. After doing a certain amount of working on the Western and Midland Divisions up to and during World World War II, they were all concentrated after the war on the old Central Division, where they were universally referred to as 'Austin Sevens' by the L&Y men.

This was a locomotive which had a lot going for it and showed considerable promise. Indeed, many of the L&Y men regarded the 'Austin Seven' as the equal of a Stanier Class 8F 2-8-0 when it came to sheer, gutsy slogging. The front end layout was good, with reasonable cylinders and an excellent long-lap Walschaerts valve gear driving the overhead piston valves, and the boiler steamed very well, despite the moderate-sized grate. Alas, their virtues were bought at a high price in availability and maintenance costs, because of grave deficiencies in the chassis design.

If ever a mess was made of producing the engine part of a locomotive, this was the outstanding example. The Class 4F frame was used as a starting point, lengthened to take another pair of wheels and 'Midlandised' up to the hilt. It was as prone to fracture as that of the 0-6-0s. Small Midland axleboxes, à la Class 4F, suffered all the latter's susceptibility to rapid development of roll in the journals, knock in the guides and heating: when running at any speed, the engine sounded rather like a set of castanets with everything knocking. The springs were real Derby specimens; they lost camber (no link adjustment to overcome the effects), the buckles shifted and the engine came down mainly at the front end until it ran along like a dog sniffing in the gutter.

Even the Walschaerts gear was an Achilles heel (among many!). The eccentric straps wore — or broke — the white metal out even faster than from the axleboxes and, aggravated by wartime maintenance, there was a long spell of trouble with the crossheads shedding their gudgeon pins, with quite spectacular results: in the late 1940s, they all had to be modified to prevent this. The heavy wear of the axleboxes also took it out of the coupling rods, which were of general Class 4F proportions: there was heavy crank pin bush wear (though I do not recall any cases of crank pin breakage such as plagued the 4Fs) and even more so at the weakest link, the coupling rod joint pins. Virtually never did these engines get beyond a 20-24,000mile exam without the rods having to go back to main works for complete overhaul.

So, attractive as their performance might be to their crews — despite the somewhat spartan conditions in their brief, far-from-protective cabs — their mechanical performance earmarked them for withdrawal as soon as they could be spared and replacements made available. The influx of WD 2-8-0s after the war provided this opportunity and they were put to the sword in large numbers from 1949 onwards, after a quite short life.

This, then, was the modern fleet which, together with the pre-grouping types, was available to work the freight service when Mr Stanier came in 1932. The LNER was running large numbers of 2-8-0s capable of handling partly fitted trains and so, too, was the GWR. The LMS had nothing bigger than the 'Crabs' and 4Fs for working such trains and it was natural that a 2-8-0 version of the other two-cylinder taper boiler engines should have been put into the hands of the Operating Dept.

All the features of the Class 5s and others were built into them — the long-lap motion, large axleboxes, carefully balanced wheels, side-bolster pony truck, excellent front end, trouble-free firebox and the large, comfortable-riding tender.

A curious feature, however, was the boiler, type 3C. In many respects it was very comparable with that on the Class 5 (Type 3B), although the need for a shorter barrel, to suit the chassis wheelbase, prevented its being interchangeable. Yet even in the firebox there were minor differences in dimensions — small fractions of an inch only — which revealed a greater affinity to the 'Jubilee' boiler (type 3A) than to the Class 5. This was even the case with the original straight-throatplate boilers, also. Why the Class 5 boiler, with the front (parallel) barrel ring shortened by about a foot, was not used is not now apparent.

The Class 8Fs were lovely machines, very much in the Class 5 tradition. Their maintenance was very reasonable indeed and there were very few troubles. During the 1950s the decision was taken, based on lengthy experience, to increase their mileage before valve and piston examinations to 40-48,000miles, which was no mean achievement for a small-wheeled engine doing some fairly fast work. The big Stanier coupled axleboxes would hardly run hot if you applied a blowlamp to them: I remember standing on Derby station one Saturday afternoon in 1953 or so, and seeing one come romping in on a Blackpool-Wellingborough special passenger train, express headlights up and spot on time. She was resplendent in new black paint after a general repair in Horwich works and could not possibly have been more than three days out of the paintshop! No doubt Bolton shed had collected her for running in on the Wednesday or Thursday, had given her one day's trials, and then sent her to Blackpool to work home on Control orders.

Come World War II, the Stanier Class 8F was adopted as the early Ministry of Supply freight locomotive for war service and orders for 230 locomotives were placed with various builders. As compared with the early LMS engines (No 8012 onwards) the connecting rods were shortened by 5in and the piston rods, slidebars, etc, lengthened to correspond. Certain engines built by the LNER were fitted with Wakefield mechanical lubricators and other altered fittings in place of the standard LMS equipment. A further modification, which was much more serious in its effects, was incorporated in some of the 'foreign-built' engines, in that the LMS coupled wheels, with built-up balance-weights, were discarded in favour of wheels with solid cast balance-weights which made no provision for balancing the reciprocating masses.

This feature was also adopted on the WD 2-8-0s designed for R. A. Riddles and it proved to be a major failing. The unbalanced reciprocating masses, while giving freedom from rail hammer-blow, resolved themselves at speeds over about 20mph into such large fore-and-aft forces, relative to the mass of the locomotive, that the engine was induced to 'shuttle'. This shuttling action was noticeable on the footplate when the engine was running with steam on, but it was not particularly objectionable until speeds of the order of 40mph were reached. It was transmitted through the buffing and drawgear of the tender to the train, where it could be very noticeable at the front end, but was gradually damped out by the buffer and drawgear springs, and friction, further back.

The fun arose, however, when the engine was coasting at speed, and particularly on falling gradients when the train was 'leaning' on the tender. The intermediate buffer springs between engine and tender were compressed until the intermediate buffing blocks came into contact: the engine block, oscillating in phase with the coupled wheels, kicked the tender away with considerable violence, only for the train to push it back into contact. The result was a brutal, bucking movement between engine and tender, usually at about 80 cycles/min, which made the enginemen's position unenviable and, if continued for any length of time, left the footplate knee-deep in coal 'jiggered' from the tender. There were only three possible ways of dealing with this purgatory — keep a breath of steam on and run in front of the train (not practicable on long falling gradients), screw the tender hand brake on hard (not effective except on easy gradients) or grin and bear it. Needless to say, it was usually a case of the latter! Latterly, the locomotives with satisfactory reciprocating balance were marked with a star on the cabside, and these could then be used on partly-fitted freight trains (at that time Class D, 50mph maximum) comfortably — and, of course, on passenger trains.

The work these engines did seldom saw any publicity. I rode on them from time to time and they always steamed well, rode very well, and were on top of the job. On the heavy mineral trains, they were driven for long periods on full regulator and up to 45% cutoff when slogging up long gradients, and thrived on it.

As an example of their work, I would mention some test runs made on coal trains on accelerated timings from Wellingborough to Brent. There were a whole series of these trains timed as Class J — those were the days, postwar, when the mines were turning out close on 200million tons a year, rather than the present 115million or so. A Class 8F was allowed to take '=55' on these trains, ie the equivalent of 55 13ton mineral wagons, or other sizes according to a conversion formula, and the journey of 60.2miles was booked in 152min, including one switch from slow to fast line (we would call it a 'weave' in modern operating parlance, but the term was unknown then). A series of three test runs were made with the load reinforced to '=60' to see whether a Class 8F could time the train under these circumstances.

I have written elsewhere* in some detail about the working of the final test run, with special reference to the skill of a driver handling a loose-coupled, unbraked train over an undulating road such as the Midland main line. Done well, this was artistry of the highest order, even if applied to some of the crudest engineering in existence. Done less than well, the results could be broken drawbars, injuries to the guard at the rear end or even derailment.

On the first trip, we had a mixed 53wagon load of 16ton and 13ton wagons of coal ('=60' 13-tonners) and the engine proved able to work to the point-to-point timings, with something in reserve. Full regulator and 35-40% cut-off were generally employed on the long 1 in 200 banks; in

*Only an Eight on a Coal Train. Trains & Railways, Volume 2, No 3

these conditions the exhaust injector was in almost continuous use and maintained the water level comfortably, the consumption amounting to a total of 3,050gal., or an average of a modest 50.7gal mile, though of course the actual rate for the time the regulator was open must have been nearer 90gal/mile.

The train was most ably driven by Passed Fireman Beswick from Wellingborough shed, with No 48365. It was a real delight to watch Beswick handling that train: it also provoked thought that the standard of skill necessary was undoubtedly higher than that to drive a West Coast Anglo-Scottish express. The guard would tell you it was, anyway! The technique of getting the slack out of a long loose-coupled train (something like 30ft of it) on the down grade in readiness to attack the next rise with it stretched, and without exceeding the stipulated speed of 35mph and without putting the guard through the rear door of his van, had been thoroughly mastered and Beswick's quiet concentration applied it faultlessly.

We would go rampaging up 1 in 200 (average) from Luton to milepost 28¼, drift down on similar grades towards Chiltern Green with just a suspicion of a brake application, until near the station the regulator would be cracked to take out the slack, each coupling gently tightening while we were still on falling grades. When, just before the Colne Valley viaduct, he was satisfied that he had the lot with him, Beswick would open the regulator step by step until the engine gave a nice crackle at the chimney top and we would go hard at it up to Harpenden Junction. The inspector riding in the van said he never felt a snatch the whole way.

The last run tested men and machine to the limit, however, for we had a train made up specially with 60 13ton wagons of wet power station slack, and our computations estimated this as 100tons heavier than the previous two runs. This meant an extra 5% almost all the time on the reverser and we failed to make booked times on the long climbs. Furthermore, we used an extra 1300gallons of water in consequence, which must have put coal consumption at about 90lb/mile or a little over, and that is not fun. Nevertheless, No 48269, which Beswick had on that day, stood up to it well, steamed immaculately and was in no way distressed.

Any review of freight locomotive power would be singularly incomplete without some mention of the WD 2-8-0s, or 'Austerities'. I make no apology for mentioning these engines in the company of LM designs, because apart from the features introduced by Mr Riddles to facilitate production under wartime conditions they were as LMS-bred as anything from the Derby drawing-boards. In fact, a number of LMS draughtsmen were seconded to North British for the design work. The starting point was, of course, the Stanier 2-8-0, with as many castings as possible eliminated, with coupled wheels designed to be suitable for cast iron (though in practice iron was abandoned quite early in favour of cast steel) and a round-top firebox on a parallel boiler barrel. Mechanical lubrication was eliminated in the interests of economy, and another feature introduced with this in mind was the absence of a smokebox ring to the barrel, resulting in a smokebox smaller in diameter than the boiler clothing. In a number of respects the design improved on the LMS model. The Midland brake valve was discarded for a 'Dreadnought' valve with separate graduable steam brake valve. The exhaust steam injector and Midland live steam injector were replaced by two 'Monitor' injectors — really first-class devices. The LMS reversing rod from the cab, a flat-section rod with a lot of 'whip', which needed a steadying bracket, was passed over for a stiff tubular rod. They were built for a short life and a gay one during the war, but that life was *so* short under wartime conditions, and there was so much sound potential in them, that there was no thought of scrapping them after hostilities ceased. Altogether some 733 2-8-0s and 25 2-10-0s were bought by the LNER and BR on behalf of several Regions, and put into heavy freight service after overhaul, enabling scrapping of much old power to be undertaken.

During 1949, while I was at Railway Executive headquarters at 222 Marylebone Road, the first distillation of experience with the 'Austerities' took place, and this led to a lengthy list of proposed modifications. Some arose from complaints through trade union channels, some were based on (bitter) maintenance experience and a few from other sources. They were of various degrees of priority: some were done at next works repair, while some never did get done because a satisfactory solution to the problem could not be devised within acceptable cost limits.

The top priority jobs included the fitting of sliding side windows and gangway doors to the somewhat spartan cabs, the restaying of the smokebox tubeplate and firebox doorplate in the upper areas to eliminate the original plate gusset stays which gave trouble, and the replacement of the water gauges by either LM or BR standard fittings. The original water gauges were absolute fiends: if the left-hand glass broke, it was almost impossible to shut off the cocks unless you were wearing asbestos gloves, so badly were the handles placed close to hot steam pipes, etc. In addition, the crosshead gudgeon pins had a nasty habit of falling out — they were not nutted, but held in by a triangular plate secured by three very inadequate studs. As they were shopped the crossheads were bored out and fitted with LM-type gudgeon pins, fitted in the body of the crosshead on two seatings of a continuous taper, and nutted and cottered on the outside — which stopped that little game. Other items need to be outlined. Enginemen had some surprises (and maybe a few injured legs) when, under certain conditions of curvature and cant, the cab fall-plates could dig into the corners of the steel tender platform and then fly up under pressure. Nasty! All the platform corners had to be reprofiled to stop this happening. The tender, too, was distinctly prone to derailment. The four axles were equalised in two pairs, but the equalising beam pins soon became seized and the weight distribution went all to pot. Various palliatives were tried, but the problem was never fully bottomed and cured. It was such a regular occurrence that, for instance, when they were taken into Crewe Works from the South shed, the tenders were solemnly filled with water before starting and emptied on arrival in the works.

Being built for an austerity age, the mechanical lubricators of the Stanier engines were replaced by oil boxes to feed the axleboxes (via a telescopic pipe arrangement that was nearly as crude as on the LNW engines) and a sight feed lubricator for cylinders and valves. There was a degree of hot box trouble as a result of displacement and fracture of the oil pipes, and on occasion the oil boxes themselves did not get the attention they warranted (there were four quite big ones on each side for the coupled boxes). The real answer was to fit mechanical lubricators delivering straight into the underkeeps, but the cost was reckoned to be prohibitive. A few were fitted with a small Wakefield 'Fountain' type lubricator in the cab for the boxes, but this was only partly successful. Consideration was given latterly to putting hoses from the original oilboxes to the underkeeps, but I do not think this ever came to fruition. There was a stupid little difficulty on the 'Detroit' cylinder lubricator, too. The filling plug was screwed into a renewable seating, the idea being that its constant use should not wear or strip the threads in the main body prematurely. Fine in theory; but in practice the seating always unscrewed with the plug. We tried all sorts of ways of fixing that seating — set screws, brazing, the lot — but it always came out with the plug after a few days.

On the credit side there was quite a lot to be said in their favour. Unkempt they generally looked, but they were rugged and reliable. The steaming was satisfactory from the start, but after a visit to the Rugby test plant which led to the fitting of slightly smaller blastpipe caps it was as near perfect as could be. There were two really good live steam injectors on them, very reliable at all times. The Laird crossheads, with bolted-on slipper, were a joy for the maintenance staff — they could have the slipper out, remetal it and have it back, without need for machining if they had the proper chills, in an hour. And while the tender, with its narrow bunker, did not give the same degree of cab protection as the Stanier 4,000gallon design, the bunker was perhaps a little better at feeding coal when part-empty, thanks to the steeper inclination at the sides. Also the 5,000gallon capacity (with no scoop) could be a godsend.

But, once again, they experienced all the shuttling trouble from total absence of reciprocating balance. It seemed particularly bad on the 'Austerities', to the point that the engine and tender drag-boxes behind the intermediate buffing blocks distorted quite seriously, and had to be stiffened up with additional gussets. We also tried to stiffen up the intermediate buffers by washering up the springs, but this was of strictly limited effectiveness. But on some of the Central Division banks, such as coming down from Copy Pit, I think if you could have fitted a straight

84

chute from shovelling plate to firehole the engine would have fired itself!

It used to be great fun at Newton Heath at summer weekends in 1955-57. The start of Oldham Wakes Week, in early June, was the best. There would be anything up to 50 specials booked out of the town on Friday evening and Saturday morning — Blackpool, Southport, Morecambe, Fleetwood, Torquay, Yarmouth and other diverse destinations — and from about the Tuesday before, the Divisional Office would be feeding into Newton Heath every 'foreign' engine that would be suitable — 'Jubilees', Class 5s, 'Crabs', 2-6-4 tanks, even Class 4Fs. All these would be mysteriously stopped 'under repair' there until Friday afternoon, when lo! they became fit again! But you could always reckon that, about 11 o'clock on Saturday morning, some irate driver would put his head round the door and say 'Guvnor! They've given me an Austerity to work the 12.30 express to Blackpool North. It's not right. Can I have something else — I'll even take a 4F.' And you'd go out into the shed, point out the vast emptiness with hardly a locomotive in sight, and say 'If you can *find* anything else you're welcome. But four others before you this morning have had to take Austerities on excursions.'

There was just one engine of the class that did not suffer this shuttling malady — No 90527, which had been experimentally modified, by riveting steel plates on the outside of the cast balance weights, to balance 40% of the reciprocating masses — the maximum that clearances would permit. I rode on her throughout one night on the 10.40pm Class E freight (not less than four wagons vacuum-braked) from Aintree to Copley Hill, a test if ever there was one — 7miles down from Todmorden, and 3miles down from Morley Tunnel (steep), as well as all sorts of short bits between. But on none of these banks, even at speeds up to 45mph, and using the graduable steam brake valve to steady the train rather than get assistance from the fitted head, could we get her to shuttle. The various enginemen involved were quite incredulous, thinking that something wonderful had been done to the intermediate drawgear to effect such an improvement (in fact, nothing had been done to it at all). She was completely cured, but it took a long time to persuade the CME that he should do anything more. Finally, he took No 90527 on some official, instrumented tests. And the finding? She was no better than other Austerities and it had not really mitigated her shuttling. We were utterly dismayed — it could only have happened by getting the wrong engine by mistake. So nothing more was heard of it and they shuttled into Valhalla. They will be remembered for their chunky bark, the gentle knock of their motion, and the many times one or two pairs of tender wheels were disengaged from the ballast.

11/Good Both Ways

At the post-war peak, LMS designs had contributed 645 2-6-4 and 339 2-6-2 tank locomotives to the overall BR fleet. In addition, the direct BR standard derivatives accounted for a further 155 and 30 respectively. This was quite a sizeable fleet, devoted to suburban, local and medium distance passenger work, ECS jobs and a limited amount of freight. After early reliance on pre-grouping designs, mostly obsolete, the LMS started building mixed traffic tank engines in earnest in 1927, and thereafter there were very few years when the LMS and LM Region were not getting a substantial influx of new engines of this general category.

Now of course the great virtue of tank engines was that you did not need to turn them at terminals, thereby saving time, shunting moves in the terminal area, line capacity and sometimes a lot of hard work, not to mention the (often difficult) space to lay down a turntable. That was very fine — just like the modern double-cab diesel or electric locomotive. But maybe you noticed, when 2-6-4 tanks and the like were around, that if there *was* a turntable at the terminal or close to it, then drivers of these locomotives would go to considerable lengths — even forego meal breaks if necessary, some of them — to get on to a turntable so that they could depart chimney-first.

The reason was quite simple, though it never figured in textbooks on operating practice: it was all a question of cab comfort. Cabs were designed to be used chimney-first, and even if they did not provide very full protection and were draughty, the draught was all behind you and going further away. When running bunker-first, on the other hand, the crew was directly in the line of fire. A keen gale would come in through the side door openings, straight on to the seated men, because normally there were no draught screens to stop it — and none could be fitted without cramping the style of the disposal men with long fire irons, which were necessarily stored on the tank top, or interfering with rearward visibility, or both. Furthermore, when the coal was part-used from the bunker, the wind would blow in under the bunker doors, laden with coal dust, and make life somewhat less than pleasant.

So for all its compactness and lower first cost, the mixed traffic tank engine was not quite so versatile as some people would have us believe. There were other deficiencies as compared with a tender locomotive, too. Water capacity was always a limiting factor, and a 2,000gallon capacity effectively limited the range between water columns to 50-60miles at the most. Adhesion was another constraint, both because it varied immensely with the state of tanks and bunker, and because of weight transfer on curves and crossings with carrying wheels fore and aft. So they always tended to be a bit light on their feet, which made them something of a liability on, for instance, trip freight work, particularly if there were any heavy grades. I wish I had as many five-pound notes as occasions when 2-6-4 tanks on North Stafford 'Loop Line' freights coming down the steep bank from Hanley — 1 in 50 odd, I believe — slithered past the home signal at Etruria and out on to the main line, unable to hold their trains. However, perhaps the real blame for that could rightly be laid on the archaic British practice of building wagons without continuous brakes.

The first of the mixed traffic tank locomotives on the LMS scene were the Fowler 2-6-4s with parallel boilers, known to some (for reasons which escape me) as Seapigs. They were designed at Derby during a period when the enlightened were in the ascendancy in the drawing office and were a great success, thanks to an excellent front end and long lap valves. They were lively, very fast and extremely economical.

There was quite a lot of 'Royal Scot' thinking about them — they were really contemporary with the 'Scots' — notably so far as cylinders, motion and running gear were concerned. The 9in valves had a maximum travel of about 6½in, and the ports were reasonably straight and free. While the circular smokebox appeared to be sitting in a full saddle, that saddle was in reality nothing more than an open box, with a projection of the cylinder casting entering it through the frames and carrying the steam and exhaust passages. The steam pipes and blast pipe then projected through the smokebox bottom to meet up with these extensions, and these points had to be made airtight with fitted makeup plates. There were a few undesirable sharp bends as a result of this construction but they did not appear to inhibit the steam and exhaust flow in any degree.

The chassis generally followed Midland practice, but the axleboxes were of better size, of manganese bronze, and were not seriously prone to heating except as a result of disturbance of the bearing strips or whitemetal. The last 30 engines — those with "limousine" cabs — were built with Stanier side-bolster bogies and trucks, whereas the others had swing-link trucks. All rode very well, however.

The boiler was, in effect, a standard Midland one from the 'Belpaire' 4-4-0s, the G8AS type, and was quite well-proportioned. There was certainly no complaint about its steaming. Tanks, bunker and cab were based on those of the old Midland 0-6-4 tanks, with the exception of having two-way water pick-up gear fitted. Altogether it was a harmonious design and footplate staff found it very much to their taste, even if it lacked some of the finer points which were to come with the Stanier engines. Indeed, some men preferred them to the taper-boiler version.

The maintenance of the parallel-boiler 2-6-4s was fairly straight-forward, though they undoubtedly did get fairly run-down after about 50,000miles. It should be remembered, of course, that LM depots (even the main concentration depots) were not equipped or staffed to renew or overhaul sets of coupled axleboxes, but only the odd box which ran hot; things were different on the old LNER, where larger depots did not think twice about renewing every axlebox at a valve and piston examination. There was a certain amount of frame fracture trouble at the coupled axlebox horns, for which the clip-up hornstays were partly responsible. The water pick-up scoops were hardly worth the candle, and could lead to a lot of tank bulging and leakage from 'sprung' rivets when overfilling took place on troughs.

Probably the major trouble experienced was with that smokebox saddle, though it did not become serious for the best part of twenty years. By the 1940s, corrosion from damp smokebox ash getting down past the pipes through the smokebox bottom had so eaten into the saddles that parts were paper-thin or non-existent and replacement was essential. Even the main frames were badly corroded in this area. The opportunity was therefore taken to remodel the whole front end on Stanier principles, with a new smokebox saddle, fabricated from plate and having the exhaust channels integral with it. After an attempt to weld up the corroded areas of the main frames, which proved abortive — both the saddle and the cylinders had to bed on to the frame plate to get a joint which was tight to exhaust steam, and this proved impossible on the welded surface, despite the most careful dressing off — new inserts were welded into the frames. New cylinders, with the steam pipe flange on top to suit pipes coming through a gland in the side of the smokebox, were fitted. This arrangement had been well proved on the taper-boiler engines, and really made a lasting job of the front end. Alas, the engines themselves were not to last more than a few years after it was done.

These engines could be cheerfully driven with a wide open regulator and cutoffs even shorter than 15%, or with the first valve only and, say, 25%, and both seemed equally effective. Their work seldom figured in the performance articles, understandably, but one run illustrative of their capabilities is worth mentioning: it was made by No 2387 on a seven-coach train of 185tons on the 8.53am Watford Junction — Euston semi-fast during the 1930s, and resulted in a maximum speed at Brent of 83½mph. The start-to-stop time for the 17.5miles, inclusive of a signal check outside Euston, was no more than 19minutes. As recently as 1963 a speed of exactly 90mph was recorded with one of them.

The Stanier 2-6-4 tanks were not usually reckoned to be quite as sprightly as the Fowler ones, though in my experience there was precious little in it. Many men were also of the opinion that they were not quite so economical on water, but I find that one hard to accept. There were depots which took a real pride in economic working: Southport men were a case in point. It was 35miles to Manchester, and on some of the lighter trains, calling at St Lukes and Wigan Wallgate only, it was a matter of honour not to exceed 750gallons for the trip. It was not hard work, mind you, but the working of the engine was kept at a nice, even level and with the strictest control against blowing off.

Of course, one can argue — and people have, in print, in the past — that to use 90ton engines to pull three or four-coach trains about was all rather ridiculous, and treated in isolation it was certainly over-generous. But many of the diagrams incorporated very much harder jobs in the course of a day's work, and the light jobs were fill-in work to get good utilisation out of the locomotive. There were plenty of places where a 2-6-4 tank had to work hard for its living, and they did so with some relish — even when the impossible was asked of them.

Take the Euston — Bletchley semi-fasts, for example. For years I used to travel from Willesden Junction to Watford on the 5.43pm from Euston, allowed 14min start-to-stop for the 12.1miles, almost all uphill; now that, with a seven-coach load of about 205tons tare, 240tons gross, wanted some doing! In fact, it was one of those impossible timings that the LMS Operating Department churned out in considerable numbers and which were extremely difficult to persuade them to abandon — 3min Preston start to Oxheys, 1.3miles, was another, and 14min Rugby start to pass Weedon, 12.9miles, was yet another, and if you are inclined to scoff, have a look at the gradient profiles! Eventually I took this particular one up with the powers that be, and getting no satisfaction or admission that the timing was even difficult, challenged them to name a date on which they would demonstrate the timing actually being achieved. But Euston buried their heads a little deeper in the nice, warm sand and replied that 'they had experienced no difficulty . . . . . .', etc.

The nearest I ever saw it approached was one day with No 42589, when a doughty Watford driver named Jimminson made it in a few seconds over 15 minutes. Even that needed full regulator, never less than 30% on the reverser at over 60mph., and a first-rate fireman backed by a pair of injectors which gave no cause for anxiety. The least little thing going wrong — an injector knocking off that needed nursing back on again, or the firehole doors a bit stiff — and you were down the Swanee. But Jimminson would roll into Willesden just as the 5.45pm 'Midlander' ran through on the fast line, and then it was hell-for-leather after him, even though the express had at least a minute start.

A machine-gun-like exhaust rattled back off every bridge or building, a just-perceptible fore-and-aft oscillation gently wagged the evening papers of the twelve (at least) individuals in each compartment of the first coach, and about Headstone Lane the rear brake first of the 'Midlander' would slide past, gradually followed by the rest of the train. Birmingham business-men would gaze glumly at the grinning faces of Watford office workers, and then as the engines drew level good-natured gestures would be exchanged between the enginemen, thumbs went up to noses, and the 5.43pm, going a steady 65 up the 1 in 339, would pass by in a blaze of glory and be standing in Watford Junction platform when its rival came through. Great days!

Another place where the taper-boilered tanks earned their corn was the Cheshire Lines route between Liverpool and Manchester, where they worked turn-and turn-about with Class 5s on the express service. The fast trains got 45min between the two Central termini, stopping intermediately at Warrington and Farnworth (now Widnes), and hauling seven or eight coaches there was no time to stand around. The timings were almost identical with those which apply to the DMUs today, and were worked to with commendable precision and reliability. Indeed, there was a useful degree of rivalry between the Trafford Park and Brunswick men who shared these workings between them. It was an unusual trip that did not produce a 70 somewhere along the line.

It was all achieved at a certain cost, naturally, and the taper boiler 2-6-4s had their weaknesses in the same way as the parallel boiler engines. From the crew's point of view, the cab gave better protection, but it was still not very good when running bunker first. What were absolute pests, particularly on stopping trains, were the live steam injectors. They were very prone to 'fly off' in the last stage of braking before a station stop. The fireman then had to shut off the steam, let the water flow for a few seconds, then gradually open the steam valve again, juggle with the water regulator and get it working again, usually just as the 'rightaway' was given. The driver would open the regulator, the engine would surge forward, and off it would fly again. Repeat of same performance!

But they rode beautifully, with their side-bolster trucks fore and aft. The Fairburn engines, with manganese steel axlebox liners, would generally go to 80-90,000miles before tyre wear dictated their withdrawal for works repair.

On the maintenance side, the side tanks brought problems. The later Fairburn engines, with redesigned, riveted tanks and no pick-up scoops, were not bad, apart from odd rivets that leaked — probably due to indifferent workmanship done in less-than-ideal conditions. How would you like to work all day in a tank about 19in wide and in parts only 3ft high, twined between baffle plates and stays, holding up hot rivets while the riveter on the outside assaulted your eardrums with a pneumatic hammer whose din reverberated round inside this steel coffin? But the long-wheelbase earlier engines, many of which had welded tanks, caused plenty of difficulty with leaking seams and bulged and fractured plates, none of which was very easy to rectify for a boilersmith at a shed with very limited resources. The plain fact was that they were, in essence, riveted tanks which were assembled by welding but had not been designed to take proper advantage of the welding process. The removal of the water pick-up gear in the 1950s was a step in the right direction, but might usefully have been taken years earlier, for the amount of necessary use of the scoop was very small.

The cylinders and valves got very dirty for the mileage run — particularly so on the Fairburn engines with self-cleaning smokeboxes — though this probably reflected their use on a rather different type of work, with heavy trains and frequent stops — and it was by no means unknown for valves to be removed at well under the laid-down 30-36,000miles examination period, due to excessive carbon build-up causing heavy valve ring or liner wear, partial blockage of ports, or ring breakage. It was hardly surprising, given the amount of coasting to stops and the very common use of full gear when doing so, that a lot of smokebox char should get sucked down the blastpipe and some should stick to a lubricated surface.

No mention of maintenance problems would be complete, however, without some reference to the Tilbury Section. Mechanical Foremen and fitters there knew just about all there was to know, from hard, practical experience, about problems and weaknesses — it was a line to test the finest that could be designed and built. Not only was the work hard, with 13coach trains the norm on an intensive service, but the water available was vile, hard and largely untreated. Boilers had to be washed out weekly instead of fortnightly elsewhere. The amount of scale produced could not be reliably washed out by traditional means, and frequently built up to the point where it was necessary to remove blocks of tubes to get at it. Tube leakage was more frequent than it should have been. And I have seen injector cones which it would have been difficult to get a No 10 knitting needle through, the scale having built up in only four weeks. Yes, the Tilbury could be rough: it cried out for electrification.

After World War II it was an almost entirely 2-6-4 tank line; pre-war, the passenger services had been shared between the three-cylinder 2-6-4 tanks and the Tilbury 4-4-2s, but as the latter became more and more outclassed they were replaced by two-cylinder 2-6-4 tanks of the short wheelbase series — and for a spell, by a couple of Fowler 2-6-4s, though that did not last long.

Now the three-cylinder tanks were built specifically for the Tilbury, and a great success story they were there — better liked by the enginemen than the two-cylinder ones. The three-cylinder drive was partially dictated by the need to minimise hammer-blow on certain weak bridges, and partly by a feeling that it might offer some advantage in acceleration from stops. Whether it was the six beats that gave them an impression of quick acceleration I am not sure, but they were certainly more sure on their feet than the later Fairburn engines. Indeed, I once or twice saw drivers start from each station in full gear by pushing the regulator handle unhesitatingly right up to the stop, without a suggestion of a slip. And the relatively low superheat did not affect the performance or steaming in any adverse way: a few got the 4C boilers with 18 or 21 superheater elements instead of the original 12, together with the 6in longer firebox, but the great majority lived with the original boilers to the end, smokebox regulators and all.

The only real modification they had in their lives, apart from the universal removal of dry sanding and its replacement by steam sanding, was to the cabs. The first 25 were built, like the last 30 parallel boiler engines, with completely enclosed cabs having full length doors with drop lights. The protection afforded was magnificent, but they got unbearably hot in summer and so the full length doors were cut down. The later engines started life with the more normal door opening and half-length doors.

Here it was that I first saw the Hudd inductive ATC in use, the fore-runner in many important respects of the present BR AWS. The Tilbury men had total confidence in it in fog, just as drivers have in its modern equivalent. In fact, one driver demonstrated it for my benefit coming back from Shoeburyness one afternoon, on sighting a distant and home on. He left the engine untouched, steam still on, and following the prescribed delay after getting the warning with no acknowledgement, the brakes went on and we came to a stand, still puffing away merrily, about 200yds short of the home signal. In those days it was still fairly novel — it had been installed pre-war, but had been allowed to lapse during the war years to economise on maintenance — yet it was clear that such a device had to come. The disaster at Harrow in 1952 was the catalyst that led to its development into BR AWS for widespread application.

The fun really started on the Tilbury Section when the Fairburn 2-6-4 tanks started to arrive in 1946. The rocking grates and self-cleaning smokeboxes were generally welcomed in an area where staff was not easy to get or to hold, though if you got a rocking grate section broken on the ashpit just before the evening rush hour started there was a certain nostalgia for the old plain grates into which you could drop the odd bar or two from outside with the tongs! But the topfeed clacks were in immediate trouble. In order to overcome the perpetual leakage problem with the earlier Stanier topfeed arrangement, a new design was provided, with the clacks in a simple one-piece casting with straightforward flange attachment of the delivery pipes from the injectors which overcame this leakage. But in it were two wing valves in screwed-in seatings (Fig 4) instead of the usual caged clack valves, and these were soon causing locomotive failures due to sticking open. Then out would come the coal hammer to administer some persuasion, which might or might not be successful in reseating the valve. Coal hammers were used nearly as much on the topfeed as in the bunker, and engines were worked home with one delivery pipe hammered flat to stop the blowback. The scaling was so bad that the valves were jamming in the seating; alternatively, they would gradually hammer the seating out of the casting until the valve could not open at all, or yet again the valve head would part company from the four wings.

A hurried experiment was mounted, reverting to the standard caged clacks fitted into the new topfeed casting, with special deep cap nuts to accommodate them (hence the little 'umbrella' on the top of later topfeed casings) and this generally stopped the trouble, being subsequently adopted on all locomotives having this type of topfeed. There was one spectacular incident, however, with one of the experimental batch. I was walking down the line from West Ham station to Plaistow shed one morning when I saw her towed on to the shed with no casing over the topfeed and apparently dead. She had arrived at Fenchurch Street towards the end of the morning peak with one clack blowing through quite seriously, probably from scale on the seat. The fireman went aloft as usual, coal pick in hand, to persuade it to behave. His first modest blows being unsuccessful, he gave it a fairly hefty whack. Unfortunately the cap nut threads were not a good fit, and this was the last straw: out it came and, with the clack cage for company, roared up through the glass of the station roof, never to be found. The boiler emptied with a frightening noise, filling the station with steam, and it was fortunate that with the release of pressure the hot water flashed off into steam and did not fall to scald passengers. Nobody was injured.

The amazing thing about the Tilbury, mind you, was that in the 1950s the Plaistow District was consistently at the head of the casualty league table, with some incredible (literally) mileages per casualty. Quite often the figures showed that there had been no casualties at all on the District for weeks on end. I am not suggesting that anyone was fiddling the books, but . . . . . !

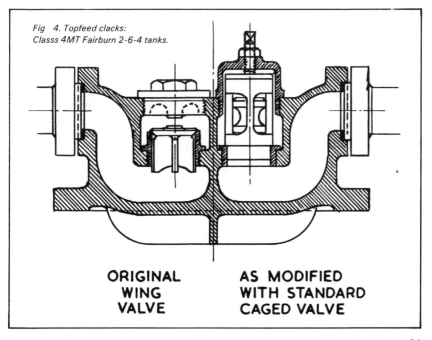

Fig 4. Topfeed clacks:
Classs 4MT Fairburn 2-6-4 tanks.

ORIGINAL
WING
VALVE

AS MODIFIED
WITH STANDARD
CAGED VALVE

So much for the 2-6-4 tanks: then there were the two types of Class 3 2-6-2s. Oh dear!

Coming just three years after the fine parallel boiler 2-6-4s, and from the same stable, one can only marvel at the complete dichotomy in thinking. Every good feature of the bigger engines was utterly rejected in the design of the parallel boiler 2-6-2s. The Midland influence reasserted itself to the full and the result was dismal in the extreme, particularly when it was allied to a tremendous effort to keep weight down.

First, there was a reversion to short-lap Walschaerts valve gear, which was about on a par with that on the Somerset & Dorset 2-8-0s of 16 years earlier. There was an early account of its suitability for short cutoff working, but it could only have been illusory. The coupled axleboxes were barely adequate even for this feeble machine, and were only saved from a lot of heating trouble by the very intermittent nature of much of the work on which these engines were used. The G6S boiler was hopelessly inadequate: the total free gas area through the tubes and flues was not more than 2.39sq ft, or 13.8% of the very small grate area, and even the tube proportion were not ideal, for the small tubes should have been 1⅝in diameter instead of 1¾in (the large tube brigade in the drawing office were still at it). Then the boiler people shrank from the modernity of going for a circular smokebox as on the 2-6-4s, and went back to a D-shaped box with a flat bottom through which the main steam pipes and exhaust channels were put, with making-up plates round them. This had to be largely replaced in the post-war years, with new cylinders to take external steam pipes and the like.

These wretched machines, which would not have supplied enough heat to mash tea in a busy refreshment room, staggered about the branch lines of the system. So long as loads were light and station stops frequent enough for the boiler to recover for the next effort, they could be lived with. But Class 3 they most definitely were not. Put them on such workings as the Moorgate-St Albans locals, with some climbing to do on trains of six or seven coaches, and they were quite lost. They were to be seen on the Midland slow line in the evenings, with the resigned City types arrayed behind them, wuffling up from Mill Hill to Elstree or from Napsbury to St Albans, doing about 35mph maximum and making a fair fuss about it. It must have been even more fun on the Widened Lines, with the blast turned into the tanks (the engines on these workings were all condensing) for tunnel work so that only the blower remained to create some draught.

Various ideas for improving the steaming of the G6S boiler were examined (incidentally, No 4 carried an LNWR chimney for a long time in the 1930s and 1940s). There was not a great deal to be gained by juggling with the tube layout, for the 4ft 1in diameter boiler barrel was just too small for a locomotive expected to do Class 3 work. The only thing that could be tried within reasonable costs was to boost the draught, despite the inadequate free gas area, to stir the fire into more animated combustion. So all were fitted with annular blastpipes working with large diameter chimneys. I think it made the steaming marginally better, but firemen were still uttering a thanksgiving when the regulator was shut; furthermore, as was to be expected, any improvement was gained at the expense of fire-throwing.

But by this time only the condensing engines for the Moorgate trains were still attempting to do Class 3 work: the rest, many fitted with vacuum-controlled regulators for push-pull working, had gravitated to very mundane branch line, empty stock and pick-up freight workings, which were all they were competent to do. As soon as the necessary DMUs came along, they were sent relentlessly to the wall.

Naturally, Stanier must have hoped to be able to make a better job of a design for the type of work envisaged. He certainly tackled the cylinders and motion, put on a long-travel valve gear with nice front end layout, and made various other detailed changes in line with his general approach. But again the boiler, tied to weight limitations, proved to be the Achilles heel. The first (domeless) boiler used on Nos 71-144 was extremely lacking, because at the time Derby was busy spacing the small tubes out well, on the theory that it would enable the steam bubbles to rise more easily to the surface and thus give a better steaming boiler. There was an extreme taper of 7in in diameter on this short No 6 boiler, and only seven flues and 135 1¾in diameter tubes could be got in. The abandonment of the wide spacing theory, and the eventual defeat of the over-large tube advocates, raised this with the domed No 6A boilers (fitted to No 145 onwards) to seven flues and 181 tubes 1⅝in diameter, but this did not produce adequate gas area either.

In 1940/41, therefore, a somewhat larger boiler was developed and fitted to four of these engines; this was the 6B, boiler, and while the firebox was the same as that of the 6A, the barrel was increased in diameter by 4in at the front tubeplate, permitting a layout of 14 flues and 171 tubes to be got in. At last this got the proportions right, as the following table shows:

Locomotives	Boiler Class	Free gas areas (ft²)			FGA as % of grate area
		Flues	Tubes	Total	
Parallel boiler: Nos 1-70	G6S	1.20	1.19	2.39	13.8
Taper boiler: Nos 71-144	6	0.59	1.70	2.29	13.1
Taper boiler: Nos 145-209	6A	0.59	2.05	2.64	13.7
Taper boiler rebuilds, No 163 etc	6B	1.26	1.93	3.19	16.6

By way of comparison, the No 7 boiler fitted to the little Ivatt Class 2 2-6-2 tanks had a total free gas area of 2.77sq ft, or 15.8% of the grate area — more than any of the Class 3s except the four rebuilds. In effect only these four were in Class 3 at all — all the others should have been downgraded to Class 2.

However, one could hardly expect the Motive Power people to face reality if it meant giving up something they thought they already had, even if it had been suggested to them. Instead, the same approach to the problem was adopted as on the parallel boiler engines, namely the fitting of an annular blastpipe and large-diameter chimney. Once again, it probably had a marginally beneficial effect, but there was no question of being able to keep both steam *and* water up between stations on anything more than about three coaches.

The 2-6-2s were the only Stanier design which was not generously proportioned in the coupled axleboxes and spring gear. Presumably this arose in building down to a severe weight limit. But hot boxes resulted on engines doing more than a bit of branch line pottering, coupled spring life was comparatively short, and the engine tended to settle down quickly, coming more heavily on to the two bissel trucks and thereby relieving the adhesion weight. They could then become very slippery customers. The tank capacity of 1,500gallons was also very limited for doing any main line work of consequence.

I touched briefly on the little Ivatt Class 2 tanks in Chapter 7. They were a great success, both mechanically and operationally. There was virtually nothing that a Class 3 tank could do that they could not do equally well. They were much speedier than the Fowler 2-6-2s, and every bit as fast as the Stanier ones. Not surprisingly, they outlasted their earlier sisters by some years at the final slaughter, and fully deserved to do so. It is very pleasing to see No 41241 preserved and doing the sort of job she was built to do.

12/The Lively 'Royal Scots'

I suppose it would be true to say that the 'Royal Scots', 71 in number, in the course of their overall life of under 40 years, made as big an impression on thinking in the locomotive world in Britain as any other class: particularly did this apply to their reincarnation following rebuilding, which started in 1943. Before the days of Pacifics, they were the mainstay of the West Coast passenger services, the big engine par excellence. In their later years, because of the limited number of Pacifics, they continued to play a major role in running the LM Region's express passenger services and came very much into their own during this period. They struck a receptive chord amongst the men who used them, and this feeling was responsible for a generally very high standard of performance.

Young readers will probably not be aware of the very great respect for the 'Royal Scots' which was felt universally during the 1930s. They took their place amongst the 'Big Four' of the passenger world with the A3s, 'Kings' and 'Nelsons', and with their big, paunchy boilers, diminutive chimneys and outside Walschaerts valve gear (which, to me, quite outshone any copper-capped chimney in fascination) they were giants in their field.

I would not wish to say anything about the origin of their design, which appears to encourage a continuing measure of controversy. The paper read by Mr E. S. Cox to the Institution of Locomotive Engineers in 1946 under the title of 'A Modern Locomotive History' went very fully into the historical aspects, and were extensively referred to in the technical railway press of the time.* Let me rather concentrate on aspects of design, maintenance and performance.

The parallel boiler 'Royal Scots' really came at a kind of watershed between the old Derby Midland tradition and the more enlightened aura of the late 1920s. As such it was not surprising that they showed a combination of strengths and weaknesses, and in the air of change which Stanier brought with him the latter had to be put right, for as the first line heavy power of the LMS they were thoroughly under the spotlight. The pressure on them became more intense with the depression in the

---

*Railway Magazine, May/June 1946 gives a summary.

early 1930s, as financial stringency dictated intensive utilisation, and this too brought deficiencies to light.

So far as the chassis were concerned, the problem areas were axleboxes, springs and bogie. The axleboxes followed later Midland practice in being of manganese bronze with pressed-in gunmetal bearing strips and whitemetal between. While generous in size (the journals were 9in diameter and 10½in long), these boxes were mechanically weak under the pounding which coupled axleboxes inevitably receive, and the hot box record became disturbing. The spring gear, too, was a sort of amalgam of Compound practice with coil springs on the leading and intermediate coupled axles and laminated springs on the trailers. The different characteristics of the two types, particularly as mileage built up, were identified as contributing to rough riding, though they were by no means the sole cause. The bogie, which initially exercised only the most gentle side control, was equally to blame. The combination of freedom for the front end to hunt, and a lack of any damping on four sets of the coupled springs, made them quite wild and unrestrained at times: this came to a head with the Weaver Junction derailment in January 1930, as a result of which the bogie side control values were doubled.

Later, in 1933, Stanier took the 'Scots' thoroughly in hand. The coupled axleboxes were replaced by the magnificent Stanier pattern cast steel type with pressed-in brass and thin continuous white metalled bearing surface. New laminated spring gear was fitted, together with the Stanier side-bolster bogie. That certainly got over most of the chassis problems.

The original parallel boiler could hardly be faulted as a device for producing steam. The 'Scots' could be driven hard or lightly, and the boiler was ready to respond and meet all requirements. Many a firehole door was never shut from end to end on a trip. The tubes were well proportioned, and the overall free gas area of 5.17sq ft, or 16.3% of the grate area, were very satisfactory figures reflecting the scope for design within that 5ft 9in dia. barrel. One could say with fair confidence — though it was never put to scientific test — that the boiler output limit would have been dictated by the draughting of the blastpipe/chimney combination. This seemed fully adequate for all that was expected in practice — and that was quite a lot — despite the very short chimney and modest petticoat. What let the side down was the smokebox generally.

This was a D-shaped box with a flat bottom, rather than a saddle. The weight was carried on the bolts which secured the bottom of the smokebox wrapper to the main frames, and the bottom plate was penetrated by the three exhaust channels and the steam pipe to the inside cylinder. All these holes had to be made good with making-up plates and packing. But corrosion and racking stresses made hay of all these arrangements to keep the smokebox airtight, and when an engine was run down the whole front end was on the move and defied all attempts, short of works overhaul, to tighten it up on any lasting basis. The standard Midland smokebox door fastening, with circumferential dogs, also had to be supplemented to avoid leakage and consequent burning.

The other great weakness, common to most LMS engines until the early 1930s, was leakage at the piston valves. The use of a broad valve ring led to serious wear and leakage, and coal consumption soared as shopping mileages were approached. The use of first four, and then six, narrow rings on each valve head tamed this defect. The front end kept very clean, as one would expect from a three-cylinder machine.

From the driver's point of view, very difficult conditions could arise from drifting steam when running. This mainly arose during light working on the first valve of the regulator — which was quite adequate for much of the work in descending the long, gentle grades of the West Coast main line. The great bluff smokebox front, rushing through the air at speed, caused a vortex action and partial vacuum alongside the smokebox, into which steam and smoke could be sucked. The driver could then be running literally blind: the only way to sight signals was to shut off. After a number of preliminary experiments with small deflectors near the chimney, which failed to get a measure of the problem, the more familiar smoke deflectors were fitted and these did the trick after various minor modifications.

When it came to work, the 'Scots' were in no way undervalued. They were expected to work right through from Euston to Glasgow, though admittedly the timings were not unduly demanding. On 'Special Limit' timings south of Carnforth, involving better than 60mph average speeds, and with the normal LMS coaching stock weighing 30 tons or just under per vehicle, 15 coaches including restaurant car could be taken, and there were no inhibitions about using them for particularly fast special workings, such as the Humber specials from Euston to Coventry and back in 1933. No 6129 came up from Coventry with 212tons gross, 94.0miles, in 79min 1sec, notwithstanding a dead stand on Camden bank for signals, and with four separate 90s on the way. Another 'Scot' with 335tons made an even more impressive run, having regard to the heavier train, for the net time on this run was no more than 77min.

But perhaps even more impressive was their sheer ability to put a shoulder to the wheel and slog on the banks. Under these circumstances they would stand a lot of thrashing. They would produce 1,400-1,500 EDBHP at almost any time for the asking, in a lumbering sort of way and with a deep-throated pulsating roar at the chimney. There is on record a run with No 6113 *Cameronian* northwards from Carlisle, with 12 coaches, 395tons gross to move, in which, after 68 at Wamphray, speed fell gradually on Beattock bank to just 30 at Greskine box, only to recover as the engine was opened out further, to 33 at Harthope and 33½ at Summit, on 1 in 75/74. This needed not far short of 1,600EDBHP, and was the highest power in service of which I have a record.

The odd man (or lady) out was *British Legion,* built to use up parts of the ill-fated 'Fury' and fitted with Stanier's No 2 boiler. She was a wonderful engine for high-speed work — if you could hang on! I used to see her regularly on a Saturday afternoon on the 2.40pm Euston-Manchester, due into Rugby at 4.8pm before the war. A Birmingham train had use of the main line platform just before this, and many a time, from a lofty perch in Rugby No 1 box, we would have the *Legion* waiting at the home signal (on that famous 44-arm gantry) at 3.59pm, nearly 10min before time, and this with 15 bogies behind the tender.

After the double chimney had proved its worth on the first rebuilt 'Royal Scots', a similar arrangement was applied to *British Legion* , along with other minor modifications. She always had a reputation of being a rough rider, however, and when the transfer of 'Royal Scots' to the Midland Division took place in 1957, *British Legion* had the dubious honour of specific exclusion from the transfer list. In all fairness it should be mentioned that she had a slightly more restricted route availability, but I have a sneaking feeling that her reputation went before her and played a part.

British Legion was at another disadvantage. Her No 2 boiler was the only one of its type: the barrel was 15in longer than the 2A boiler on the other rebuilt engines, and there was even an odd ½in in diameter at the front tubeplate. As a result, when she went into Crewe Works for general repair, the boiler was stripped off for overhaul and the chassis was dumped outside the erecting shop for two or three weeks, until boiler repairs were nearing completion. This meant she was always a much longer time in works than comparable engines.

In 1942 two 'Jubilees', *Phoenix* and *Comet,* were reboilered with the big 2A boiler. By this time, the original parallel boilers on the 'Scots' were 15years old, and complete renewal would be required within, say, 10 years. The decision was therefore taken to rebuild the 'Scots' with the same boiler and to bring them into line with modern practice in other respects, notably the cylinders and front end generally.

The rebuild was pretty extensive, though some people have credited it with elements which were not in fact new. New frame plates were provided, though almost all the stretchers were used again. New cylinders, very similar to those on *British Legion,* were fitted, the middle one incorporating a proper smokebox saddle: these had very nice straight ports and the steam and exhaust passages gave a high degree of internal streamlining. The original coupled wheels and motion were reused, together with the bogie and tender with which Stanier had endowed them.

The new tapered boiler, the type 2A, was beautifully proportioned. Slightly smaller at the smokebox end than the G10¼s boiler it replaced, the taper of the barrel made it larger at the firebox end, where the diameter could be put to better use. The firebox was the same length as before, and was one of those elegant Swindon/Stanier boxes with gentle curvature on the outer and inner wrappers continuously above the ogee bends. The 28 flues and 198 small tubes provided a free gas area of 5.10sq ft, virtually identical with that of the parallel boiler, but the tube proportions were rather better, as a result of a shorter length between tubeplates and other changes.

To set the seal on the rebuild, a double blastpipe and chimney were set in the smokebox — perfectly plain but most effective. The blast was fairly keen, and any thin patches in the fire, especially when working hard, would result in considerable pyrotechnics at the chimney, though the sound was quite quiet, neither thin and rasping as were the Gresley Pacifics with the Kylchap double exhaust, nor the deep roar of the parallel boiler engines, but something decently in between.

In practice, unless spectacular results were consciously sought, they were usually fired mainly on the back (horizontal) half of the grate, with a fairly thick fire above the bottom of the firehole and well piled in the back corners beyond the smokeplate; this was sufficient, in conjunction with the back damper only, to keep the front end of the slope fed and minimised the fireman's work. On the fairly easy 'Limited Load' timings, which could largely be kept (even with 15 coaches) on the first valve of the regulator, this was perfectly adequate to produce all the steam required and the firehole doors were seldom closed fully. When a real effort was to be made, however, there was need for a bit of air through the front damper also and then the fireman had to fire the grate more uniformly.

This LM Region trait of running on the back damper and firing mainly the back end of the grate gave fierce combustion in this area, and in time a certain amount of cinder-cutting was in evidence on the ogee bend of the copper firebox over the rear 2-3ft. If you looked at the firebed through welding gogles when the engine was working, you could see the fire in a semi-fluid state in these areas and almost appearing to boil. On one trip on a rebuilt 'Patriot' from Crewe to Euston, I watched a continuous eruption of white-hot coke drawn up through the fire on each side which built up above the general fire level in a couple of mounds. The fireman could not feed the back corners with fresh coal — the draught was almost doing it for him — and any attempt to place coal there failed because it rolled off these mounds; that was exceptional (the 'Patriots' were more prone to this than the 'Scots', for some reason) but certainly that double chimney stirred things up actively in those areas.

My first introduction to the rebuilt engines took place one Saturday afternoon in 1942, when travelling home from Tamworth to Rugby on a miserable wartime semi-fast. Speaking to the driver at Rugby I asked what his 'new' steed was like. 'Rough', came the laconic reply. 'But she's only just out of shops', I pointed out. 'Can't help that', he grumbled, 'she's still rough'. Later I was to find out just what he meant!

By 1947 this uncomfortable trait had become serious. Deferred track maintenance, and the uncanny ability of the 'Scots' to find weak track and tell the enginemen all about it, were resulting in strong complaints from footplate staff, premature shopping and extra maintenance work at the sheds, without producing any improvement. A full-scale investigation was therefore started and I was detailed to live with the 'Scots' exclusively and find out what made them tick. The next two months were spent at Longsight, Camden and Crewe North sheds, checking lateral clearances on coupled axleboxes, axlebox top clearances, condition of bogie slides, check springs and the like, besides checking drivers' reports and riding with the engines after examination.

It was really hopeless to try to divine drivers' experiences from the repair cards they submitted. The average card just said 'engine rides rough', elaborated perhaps to 'not fit to be on passenger work' if the driver felt particularly aggrieved by it. But in what way was it rough? Did it roll like a ship in a cross swell? Did it have a vicious side-ways kick at the cab end? Did it just feel as though it were running on cobblestones or the sleeper ends? Was there a violent knock in the boxes? Or some dastardly combination of these faults? That was up to me to find out; to the average driver it just 'rode rough' and from there it was a case of either crystal ball-gazing or getting out with the engine. I need hardly say which way my inclination lay.

During that period there was some distinctly 'soft' track on main lines, and you knew in advance that certain spots would give you a rocky ride. Some engines would be worse than others, and some were devils incarnate. One day I rode on No 6121 on the (then) 2.45pm from Euston as far as Stoke, and in a known spot in the vicinity of Polesworth the engine suddenly went into a prolonged series of violent tail-wagging oscillations allied with heavy rolling, made to sound even worse by loud grinding noises as the trailing wheel rims bore hard against the sides of the firebox expansion angles. We were doing 65-70mph at the time, and the fireman was just commencing his swing when it started. His shovel hit the outer edge of the open firehole door, the coal went on the floor near the leg guard, with his shovel lying in the corner of the cab at my feet. Many times I saw similar incidents, though not quite so violent as that one, and the drivers would shut off and make a brake application until the oscillation stopped.

The front end did its normal slight nosing rather like any other class, and there was a degree of occasional rolling which one expects, but given certain conditions of track, speed, and drawbar pull the engine would suddenly go berserk (or so it seemed). A soft spot in the track would initiate a roll which would tend to slew the front end round slightly; the bogie would try to pull it back, the soft coupled springs failed to check the roll, and the whole movement was transferred to the cab end in the form either of heavy oscillation, kept up intermittently for perhaps a mile, or vicious and unpredictable sidekicks.

It was during this period that I had two relatively narrow escapes. I was down to Camden one morning, measuring up three or four 'Scots' before riding with one on an afternoon train. But a driver I knew said he was going out on an earlier train, taking an engine I had just examined, so I changed my plans and rode with him instead. The train I was intending to travel on was derailed at Denbigh Hall that afternoon, due not to any fault of the engine but to track buckling in the heat of a cutting. Then, having been out from Rugby to Stoke one day, I was sitting in the office next morning getting the paperwork on the move when a telegram came in advising that the 8.30 out of Euston had been derailed at speed at Polesworth. My immediate thoughts were of that violent afternoon at that very spot, and that it must have been a 'Scot' involved. But no — it was a 'Duchess' that succumbed to that bad stretch of track.

One thing which influenced the picture was an act of deliberate policy on the LMS, following Stanier's experience on the Pacific Locomotive Committee in India, to stiffen up the bogie side control on most standard classes. Unlike the swing-link bogie, where the resistance to side movement only starts to build up significantly *after* the bogie has moved from the centre position, the spring-controlled side bolster bogie used on GWR and LMS taper-boiler engines had a substantial resistance to movement right from the start, and in the case of the 'Royal Scots' this had been deliberately increased to between 4 and 5tons. Now there were no infallible rules for arriving at the optimum value: it was inevitably a compromise, as so often happens in locomotive engineering. On the one hand, insufficient guidance from the bogie would allow the engine to 'nose', possibly for that nosing to build up into a rhythmic swing if the motion was not damped out (and if such 'hunting' took place you were really in for trouble, as the Pacifics in India were); this led to excessive flange wear on the leading coupled wheel tyres. The other extreme was to pile on the side control to the point of almost locking the bogie: the usual outcome of this was to transfer the movement to the back end of the engine due to the bogie's inability to accommodate itself to movements initiated by track irregularities and wheel tread coning.

Yet another factor came to light. The wheel boss faces, in time, suffered a certain amount of wear and re-machining, which made it necessary to thicken up the axlebox facing to compensate. With white metal there was a limit to the thickness which could be applied before it became unduly weak and either extruded or broke up under the awful beating it had to withstand with the engine running at speed. Crewe works, therefore, were in the habit of fitting a gunmetal liner on the axlebox face, secured by riveted studs, but it soon became apparent that these liners did not stay tight on the box for long, and in a number of cases they dropped off altogether. You could not inadvertently provide an additional ½in or more of side clearance on the trailing wheels without the effect being distinctly noticeable on the footplate!

After weeks of riding on 'Scots' up and down the West Coast main lines, until my ribs bore the impression of every cabside beading, I came to the conclusion that three things were needed to cure the trouble so far as the engines were concerned (the rest was up to the permanent way people!). Firstly, stiffer coupled springs were required to minimise the rolling. Secondly, the pernicious practice of fitting gunmetal liners should cease, and a steel-plate welded on to the axlebox face should be provided. Thirdly, the bogie check springs should be made softer and friction damping introduced on the bogie slides.

To say that these recommendations met with little enthusiasm would be to exaggerate. No 1 was acceptable, but No 2 was unpopular with the workshop people; No 3 was so directly contrary to what had been done for years deliberately that it caused serious indigestion. When he read my comprehensive report, E. S. Cox was so sceptical that he borrowed a suit of overalls and went out to see for himself, riding 'Royal Scots', but when he came back he opined that there might be something in what I had said after all. The result was the lengthy trials between Derby and Buxton with No 46120, festooned in cables from recording devices fitted on the axleboxes and bogie, and the flange force recording car. As a result of these tests, it was found that the best all-round results were obtained from bogie check springs giving only 1½ tons initial control, in conjunction with unlubricated friction damping pads on the bogie side bolsters. You may imagine how heartened I was when it was agreed to modify all the engines to correspond.

The coupled springs originally fitted to the rebuilds were 14-plate affairs, somewhat on the weak side, soft and quick to lose camber. This was a major contribution to rough riding. At the time of my investigation these had mostly been replaced by a 15-plate type, which were better but not the whole answer.

By the time the trials with No 46120 were coming to a conclusion, the BR standard designs were on the board, and the spring design concept of these was then tried on the 'Scots' — 16-plate springs with greater theoretical deflection per ton but seemingly an awful lot of internal hysteresis. They certainly steadied the riding, but it then became distinctly 'solid' and hard. On Nos 46146 and 46166, the two engines experimentally fitted, you could very nearly count the stones of the ballast, and this was somewhat wearing for enginemen. In the end a more acceptable compromise was adopted.

Even after all this work had been done, however, there were still the occasional black sheep. No 46131, then at Longsight, was one, and No 46120 at Crewe North became another. We tried everything, including stiffening up the intermediate buffer springs between engine and tender, to steady the back end of the engines by the weight of the tender, but with little success. It was a bug in certain engines only, and each seemed to react differently. Ultimately, it was decided to check the coupled wheel balancing on the rotating machine at Crewe, and then things began to come to light. The original wheels with solid cast balance weight had been tinkered with in early years by adding small auxiliary

33 *(Top)* Stanier 2-6-4T No 42483, fresh from General Repair, in Crewe Works, 18 May 1958./*G. Wheeler*

34 *(Above)* Three cylinder 2-6-4T No 42507 at Derby, 1 April 1958./*P. H. Groom*

35 *(Top)* Fairburn 2-6-4T No 42198 at Derby,
31 October 1961. Note the 'top-hat' on the
topfeed cover to clear the caps over the caged
clacks./*A. Swain*

36 *(Above)* Fowler Class 3MT 2-6-2T No 40060,
fitted with vacuum-controlled regulator, on
Willesden shed, 24 May 1959./*P. H. Groom*

37 *(Top)* Fowler 2-6-2T No 40028, with condensing gear and Weir feed pump for working over the Widened Lines, at Kentish Town, 20 May 1958. By this time a modified front end with outside steam pipes has been fitted./*R. A. Parting*

38 *(above)* Stanier Class 3MT 2-6-2T No 40116 on Newton Heath shed in June 1960. Retaining the low-superheat boiler without dome, the engine carries the large-diameter chimney with angular blastpipe./*J. E. Wilkinson*

39 *(Above)* 'Royal Scot' 4-6-0 No 6102 *Black Watch* as built in 1927 at the Queens Park works of North British Locomotive Co. Note the crosshead vacuum pump and bogie brakes, both features which were subsequently removed./*BR*

40 *(Below)* 'The Legion'. No 46170 *British Legion*, in early BR days, climbs out of Preston with an afternoon Euston-Carlisle train. Apart from the double chimney, she is very much in the condition as rebuilt in 1935./*Eric Treacy*

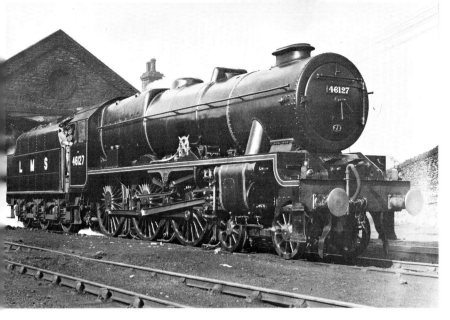

41 *(Above)* Rebuilt 'Royal Scot' No 46127 *Old Contemptibles* on Holyhead shed in 1948, in final LMS black/maroon livery but with BR numbering./*Eric Treacy*

42 *(Below)* Rebuilt 'Royal Scot' No 46108 *Seaforth Highlander*, fitted with the standard smoke deflectors, on the down 'Thames-Clyde Express' on the Mennock curves near Sanquhar in July 1957. The engine is working with a mere breath of steam and the smoke deflectors are failing to lift the smoke clear, even with no side wind./*W. J. V. Anderson*

43 *(Above)* No 46131 *The Royal Warwickshire Regiment*, a notorious rough rider in her time, awaits the right-away at Manchester (London Road) on the 4.5pm to Euston, before the trip referred to in the text./*Author*

44 *(Left)* Typical BR standard cab — in this case Class 4MT 4-6-0 No 75000. Note the mangle-wheel reverse, the 'oil/no oil' gauge (top right in the driver's cluster) and the wheel controls for the dampers/*BR*

45 *(Above right)* BR standard Class 5MT 4-6-0 73063 on Polmadie shed, 15 September 1955./*P. J. Kelley*

46 *(Right)* A grimy 'Britannia' class 4-6-2, No 70054 *Dornoch Firth*, on Holbeck shed, 9 August 1961./*G. W. Morrison*

47 *(Above)* BR standard Class 9F 2-10-0 92203
on Oxley shed. Note the very shallow depth over
the trailing coupled wheels, necessitating side
raking doors to the ashpan — here seen in their
normal open position! Note also the reversion
from the Eastern Region square fixing of the
return crank to the LM Region four-stud
design./*R. N. Hedges*

48 *(Below)* BR standard Class 4MT 4-6-0 No
75078, with double chimney, on Eastleigh shed,
9 May 1965./*P. L. Simpson*

weights, but they had never been spun again as a check. In addition, the old fluted 'Vibrac' coupling rods had been superseded by flat-section rods on some engines, only to be replaced in turn by new fluted rods in fine-grain manganese-molydenum steel, and the weights differed somewhat. So the coupled wheels of all the 'Scots' were rebalanced as they went through the shops; and thereby that particular ghost seemed to have been laid effectively.

In 1947 there was another complaint about the rebuilt 'Scots' — the obscuring of the driver's vision by drifting steam and smoke. In my experience, if the engine was being worked on the main valve of the regulator, no matter how short the cut-off, the steam would always clear itself even in bad cross-wind conditions, but high-speed running on the first valve only at 15% cut-off was frequently a nightmare, with the driver either having to cross the cab or to shut off steam for signal sighting. As a result, No 46115 was fitted with 'blinkers' and I was sent to report on their effectiveness.

On my first trip out of London with her, the weather was tailor-made for the job — damp, with slight mist and a gentle breeze from the east. As we came down from Tring to Bletchley on first valve of the regulator and 15% cut-off at about 70mph, the breeze nicely rolled the steam from the chimney top down the driver's side of the boiler, into the vacuum created by the smokebox front, and along in front of the cab in one continuous wall. Improvement in visibility—nil! The smoke deflectors were entirely the wrong shape to function properly, which they should do by catching sufficient air in front of the smokebox and guiding it smoothly alongside the smokebox and boiler barrel. This prevented a partial vacuum being formed alongside the smokebox, caused by the bluff smokebox front, into which the exhaust was drawn down from the chimney. The deflectors fitted to No 46115 were inclined at the front, restricting their 'gathering' capacity in front of the smokebox, and were too short to guide the air stream effectively before release at the back.

I put in a scathing report and pointed out that at cut-offs in the vicinity of 15 per cent, on the first valve of the regulator, they were quite useless. But I was not prepared for the official reaction of the Motive Power Department, who professed entire satisfaction with them and claimed that these engines were never driven in the manner I had described. I promptly checked my records of the previous 20 trips from Euston to Rugby and confirmed that, on the downhill stretches, the engine in no fewer than 18 cases had been worked on the first valve with cut-offs of 15% or less, which was perfectly adequate for 'limited load' timekeeping with 15 bogies on a 1 in 330 gradient. It was all to no purpose, however — all except No 46106 were fitted with the self-same deflectors. No 46106 got a pair of BR standard type deflectors, squarer at the front and not far short of twice as long. She was a Scottish engine and I had no chance to ride her, but it is my guess that this design was very much more effective.

The late 1940s were a period in which rocking grates, hopper ashpans and self-cleaning smokeboxes were being applied to all new construction on the LMR, and it was natural that the rebuilt 'Scots' should also incorporate them. It was soon found, however, that a self-cleaning smokebox was not quite so straight-forward to apply to a three-cylinder engine as to a two-cylinder one, and No. 46161, the first to be fitted experimentally, underwent trials for several years before the three-fold requirements of clean smokebox, clean tubes and unimpaired steaming were mastered. Only a small minority of the 'Royal Scots' got the self-cleaning smokeboxes before the advent of diesels caused the writing on the wall.

This chapter has, perhaps, rather dwelt on difficulties and weaknesses, and given a somewhat gloomy impression. If so, it is unintentional, for despite certain development problems on the mechanical side, there was no doubt that, within its class (ie a narrow-firebox, large passenger engine) the 'Scot' was unexcelled in this country; I say that, 'Kings' and 'Castles' notwithstanding. It steamed well, it could be made to ride well, it would sprint, its power output at speed on short cut-offs had to be seen to be believed and it was economical.

As a typical example of sound day-to-day 'Royal Scot' work, I can hardly do better than to quote a performance by Maurice Corbett of Edge Hill on the 2.10pm Lime Street-Euston in 1954, not long before he retired. He was undoubtedly one of the great Edge Hill drivers of that period — a quiet but humorous man on the footplate, ever ready for a bit of banter and leg-pull, and Stan Walls, his fireman, responded well to it: the latter was a keen model railway operator and given to wearing an American 'engineers' washable blue-and-white striped long peaked cap instead of his issue grease-top cap. What a fine team! The engine was 46164 *The Artist's Rifleman* and although the loading, at 414tons tare, was some 60tons short of the 'special limit' load permitted south of Weaver Junction, the engine's mastery of the task left no doubt that another two coaches would still have been handled with consummate ease.

Rugby, 111.1 miles from Liverpool and allowed 124min, was reached over 3min early and in a net time of 114½min, despite some deliberate easing because of an early tendency to prime and to avoid running too early. Acceleration from the Crewe slack was to a sustained 49 on Madeley bank (1 in 177), the main valve of the regulator partly open and 22% on the reverser producing some 1,580 EDBHP. Then from Rugby, the 82.6miles were reeled off in a net time of 75¾ min; despite an almost dead stand for a block failure at Hemel Hempstead, a heavy permanent way slack at Bushey, and signals on at Queen's Park we improved on the 84min booking by a few seconds in *actual* running time. There were no high speeds downhill — 78 was the maximum, very typical of West Coast running — but the uphill work was fine. From passing Bletchley at 73, speed was maintained between 70 and 72 on the slightly rising grades to

Sears Crossing, using the main regulator valve and 16% cut-off. Here it was advanced to 20%, which cleared Tring summit at 64: this corresponded to an output of 1,500EDBHP. And the overall cost: a water consumption of 6,500gallons throughout, or 33.6gal/mile, equivalent to perhaps 43lb coal/mile.

It would not do, however, for readers to suppose that footplate work was always as straightforward and rewarding as that. Would that it were! I have mentioned the rough riding anguish caused by No 46131, a Longsight engine, and one afternoon I rode her on the 4.5pm, Manchester (London Road)-Euston, stayed and came back with her on the down 'Comet' next morning. On the up journey she had been very shy for steam, as a result of which we dropped about 8min, and I quite expected her to be fetched off the diagram at Camden that night, but she turned up at the head of 13 bogies at Euston next morning for the 9.45am departure. The driver reported that she had been steam-tested and nothing had been found wrong — another way of saying that the fitter thought she should make it back to her home shed for attention rather than be stopped at Camden. The only way, then, was to make as perfect a fire as possible with good lump coal, start off with a full boiler, and cross our fingers.

Up to Hemel Hempstead we went in fair style, working easily on the first valve and 22%, and by allowing the water level to creep down very gradually, pressure was kept up to 220lb/sq in or more. But by then, with the water down to less than half a glass, the fireman had not much latitude to continue this approach. We cleared Tring in just over 37min, at 58mph, and a permanent way slack in Tring cutting put off the agony a little longer. But by Leighton Buzzard, with the water just over half a glass, pressure was down to 160 and it was a case of fighting every inch of the way — shut off the injector, tickle her palate with four or five shovelsful at a time, shut the firedoor tightly, glance anxiously at the pressure gauge which, with respite from the injector, recovers to 180, then put on the exhaust injector again until the pressure has taken another beating. Firing over the firehole flap where possible, to keep the box warm, and some real artistry with the shovel and coal hammer, had her going in this fashion all the way to Lichfield, with the additional brief help of the slack for Rugby to get some water into the boiler; but it was gruelling and dispiriting work for the fireman and imposed additional worry on the driver.

By Colwich we were on our beam ends, with only 160lb/sq in on the clock, a third of a glass of water and three very long faces. We turned on to the direct Stoke line, which climbs mostly at 1 in 300-odd, at 20 from the junction, giving thanks for the fitter who had last examined the small ejector, for surprisingly this was maintaining 20in of vacuum with such low boiler pressures. The same technique was continued all the way; sparing use of the exhaust injector just to keep the water in sight, pressure up and down, but always more down than up, until, when we shut off for Stoke, the clock was showing only 125lb and the water, dropping due to the closure of the regulator, set like the evening sun in the bottom nut of the gauge, out of sight save for an occasional surge. The large ejector was on by this time to hold the brakes off. The blower remained hard on, both injectors were quickly on to get some water into the boiler and take care of any surge while stopping, and we gently expired in Stoke, after a most careful stop, with 130lb and the water just in sight again! There was no carpeting for scorching the lead plugs, either, but we had dropped 8¾ min in running. Subsequent examination at Longsight revealed several superheater element joints blowing badly, which fully accounted for No 46131's shyness for steam. I could not help thinking that the Camden examining fitter must have been a descendant of one I knew at a certain Midland Division shed before the war with a black patch over one eye and a long-handled wheeltapper's hammer, who always looked the other way before hitting anything.

Quite the most remarkable run I have ever seen recorded behind a rebuilt 'Royal Scot' took place in 1954, southwards from Crewe on the up 'Shamrock' express. The engine was our old friend No 46164 again, but the crew were not identified: the load was a punishing 16 coaches, very full and grossing 585tons, and a late start from Crewe provided the incentive for a major effort.*

The fire must have been magnificently prepared and tended, and there could have been no question of back damper only. This heavy train was worked up to 50mph at Betley Road, and No 46164 was then put at the 3 miles of 1 in 177 to Madeley in such a fashion — I estimate about 40% cut-off, which must have produced spectacular sounds at this speed — that further acceleration took place to 51½ at Madeley, and 55 at Whitmore on easier grades. The equivalent DBHP must have been of the order of 1950, which is the highest recorded in service with one of these remarkable locomotives, weighing no more than 83tons.

The 18 'Patriots' and two 'Jubilees' rebuilt with the 2A boiler were, from a practical point of view, identical to the rebuilt 'Scots', despite their 17in cylinders. They were driven in the same way, with perhaps very marginally longer cut-offs, and their performances were indistinguishable. They did not suffer the early rough-riding reputation of the 'Royal Scots', because early modifications to the latter could be incorporated in them from birth, and were accordingly regarded even more highly by a proportion of enginemen. Some of them got manganese steel liners on the axleboxes, which was a help.

By 1962 or so, all these rebuilt engines had been demoted to mundane tasks, even pickup freight work, and by 1965 the end had come, save for the two which have been preserved. May those two long be a reminder of their gruff voices, the musical ring of their motion and the smell of their hot breath. The steam locomotive could have an infinitely less suitable memorial.

*See *Railway Magazine*, October 1963.

13/BR Standard Locomotives: The Aim and the Reality

I suppose it was inevitable that, once the railways were nationalised and became, at least in theory, a unified organisation, we should have standard locomotives to work on them. The old company traditions and loyalties, nowhere more evident than in the locomotive field, were perhaps too strong for any single company's practice to be imposed on the others successfully, save by an immensely strong character with quite dictatorial powers — something we were unlikely to experience in the climate of a publicly-owned body. Nationalised industries do not work that way; their inevitable close links with Government departments and the democratic processes would hardly allow them to do so even if the wish existed. Their use of the committee system, albeit under strong central guidance, is necessarily aimed at getting consensus agreement, and probably there were few locomotive engineers who would have said, with hand on heart, that the particular breed of locomotive with which they were concerned could not have been improved by the incorporation of some ideas from other stables. The course was set for hybrid designs, incorporating existing and new features and practices in varying proportions.

The Railway Executive was formed on 1 January 1948 to run the newly-unified railways under the overall guidance of the British Transport Commission, with executive responsibility for locomotive matters places under Mr. R. A. Riddles. Riddles' background was LMS, apart from his Ministry of Supply activities during World War II, and it was perhaps to be expected that he would assemble a team of officers at Headquarters with a strong LMS flavour. On the locomotive side there was R. C. Bond, ex-Crewe and Nelson Street HQ, Derby, and as Executive Officer (Design) came E. S. Cox, for whom I had worked at Derby when he was Chief Technical Assistant to the CM&EE. Within two years all plans were laid for a fleet of standard steam locomotives, of twelve types covering the whole power range, for construction commencing in 1951. I played a modest role in this process as E. S. Cox's technical assistant at HQ during three formative years. A total of 999 BR standard locomotives were built before construction ceased in 1960: the most numerous class (the Class 9F 2-10-0s) ran to 251 locomotives, while the least numerous, the three-cylinder Class 8P 4-6-2, amounted to a single example only.

The rationale behind the new locomotives was clearly stated by E. S. Cox in his preliminary report of June 1948. They would have only two cylinders unless the required power dictated more; in that case three cylinders would be used rather than four. They would be simple and rugged to withstand post-war conditions, mechanically reliable and able to run to high mileages between works overhauls. They would have the biggest boilers compatible with weight and loading gauge limitations. They would be sure-footed, with no low adhesion factors. The cabs would provide a high degree of comfort and protection for the crews. They would have all the latest fitments to give ease of preparation, disposal and maintenance.

This sounded a tall order to apply over a whole range of locomotives, from the biggest on the most exacting duties to the smallest on a local trip job, and yet the LMS and the LM Region, after it had gone a long way in charting such a course, had made a start in following it.

Of the twelve types, five could be said to be directly derived from very similar and modern LM Region machines — the Class 5 4-6-0, the 2-6-4 tank, the Class 4 2-6-0 and the two Class 2 types. One (the Class 4 4-6-0) was itself a derivative of the 2-6-4 tank. The remainder could be said to be entirely new. So in making any assessment of the BR standard locomotives, it is necessary, admittedly with all the benefits of hindsight, to judge them against the corresponding LM Region type, where there was one, or by their contribution to solving a problem which the LM Region, under different constraints, tackled by other means. These were undoubtedly the criteria applied by LM Region enginemen, anyway, and in large measure by the servicing and maintenance staff also.

Much of the detailed design benefited from existing Regional practices, with LM Region features perhaps more frequent than those of the others. A number of new general features were introduced, four of which had to be changed with alacrity in the light of early experience. These were the Hulson rocking grate bars, the system of cylinder lubrication, the intermediate drawgear between engine and tender, and the layout of the back end of the cabs on the tender engines.

Now the LM Region considered that it knew, with some experience behind it, how to make a fairly reliable rocking grate section, quite plain and with 'teeth' on the front and rear edges to bite into any clinker that might form or get stuck in the bars. The air space through such bars was not significantly different, either in shape or area, from that with a plain fixed bar grate, and it suited the general practice with hand firing of running with a fairly thick fire and only cleaning it during disposal on the shed. On the other hand the Hulson grate used at first on the standard locomotives was designed — and I believe was very successful — for stoker-fired engines which invariably ran with thin, even fires; with these it was possible to observe any build-up of patchy clinker and, by stopping coal delivery to that point, burn the clinker away. But in the Hulson bars, the air passages were cast within the bars, were narrow, and turned through a right-angle to diffuse the primary air sideways into the fuel bed; these just choked up with fused ash and clinker under thick, hand-firing conditions, and it was quite impossible to get out. The only possible action was to scrap the bar elements and fit new ones — and they could be just as bad after the next trip! So they were all taken off and an adaptation of the LM Region section, using separate fingers threaded on to the Hulson rocker bar, used instead. That did the trick, but mechanically it was not better than the one-piece section used on the LM engines, if as good.

Then the cylinder lubrication. The LM engines had, since Stanier's arrival, standardised a very effective system of atomised lubrication to the valve chests, controlled from the cylinder cocks so that the atomising steam only flowed when the cocks were shut. The feed to the cylinder barrels, piston glands, etc, was not atomised but fed 'solid' to the requisite points. All this was altered on the standard engines, to a regulator-controlled system adapted from the GWR system, though of course using a mechanical lubricator instead of a sight-feed one. In front of the driver was placed a pressure gauge with a green sector marked 'Oil' and a red sector marked 'No Oil'. It was in fact a steam chest pressure gauge, though not explained as such, and when running the driver was supposed to keep the needle in the green sector by keeping the regulator open, even slightly when coasting.

Well, of course no driver took this gauge seriously at all. There it was saying 'No oil', but there under the platform in front of him he could see the handle of the mechanical lubricator going round perfectly normally. The lubricator was delivering oil: *ergo*, that oil must be getting to the cylinders, no matter what the stupid gauge was saying, and it must be the gauge that was faulty. But of course the point was that the oil was certainly being delivered from the lubricator as far as the atomiser, when coasting with the regulator closed, but there was no atomiser steam to carry it thence to the valves and (on the BR standard engines) the pistons also.

As a result, some of the valve rings and liners on the Class 5s at low mileages had to be seen to be believed. The Blackpool engines were perhaps the worst, working, as they did, mainly stopping trains to Manchester or over the East Lancashire line with fairly hard working on the gradients interspersed with plenty of station stops and coasting. It was nothing to get irregular wear $\frac{3}{32}$in deep across the port bars in the liners at 10,000miles — you would think some madman had been at work with a portable grindstone in the area — and the valve rings looked like a first stage towards making a string of beads. It was just no use — the only possible course of action was to scrap the whole idea and revert to the LM Region's cock-controlled atomisers, and this was quickly done.

The cab for the big tender engines was given a lot of thought, and a full-size mockup of the 'Britannia' cab, with the front portion of the tender, was produced and installed in 222 Marylebone Road, where it was shown to management and trade union representatives and comment invited. The big feature of this mockup was a one-piece foot-plate extending back almost to the front bulkhead of the tender, thus providing a steady platform for the fireman to work on instead of firing with one foot hampered by a moving fallplate between the engine and tender footplates. This was extremely laudable. Unfortunately (and this was not realised by anyone who saw that mockup) that left a gap about 6in wide between the back of the footplate and the tender bulkhead, and an even wider one each side behind the gangway doors. In through these spaces, when running, there blew something like an icy hurricane, to the great discomfort of the enginemen, who had already had all the nice, warm pipes and valves moved out of the cab on to the firebox sides for their greater comfort. All these engines therefore had to be modified, using a small fallplate on the tender front, and unsightly canvas curtains behind the handrails, to arrest the draught.

The one-piece footplate did have its advantages, too, when the intermediate drawbar broke. This happened at least twice in service, and with a conventional floor the fireman, if firing at the time, would probably have fallen off and been killed. The trouble was the use of a screwed drawbar à la Eastern Region, nutted at the back of the tender dragbox and without safety links. Fatigue soon set in, the drawbar fracturing (as might be expected) at the threads. There was an urgent programme of dragbox alterations to adapt them for the LM-type slotted drawbar between two plain pins, and with safety links and massive intermediate buffers each side. Everything then settled down to a relatively peaceful life.

There were all sorts of other minor nonsenses. The chime whistle of the 'Britannias' was apt to fall off due to fracturing of the base, which needed to be strengthened. Oil pipe joints, which were made by forming the pipe end in dies rather than with brazed-on cones, were most unsatisfactory, either breaking off or pulling out of the nuts, and a reversion to the more usual cones was needed.

Two things probably infuriated enginemen more than anything else. These were the 'mangle-wheel' reverser and the various steam cocks operated from the cab.

Now I have no strong views about wheels as against the Midland-type double-handled crossbar reverser, incorporating the locking catch in one handle, which was used on most LMS designs. (The 'Crabs' and 'Patriots' used a wheel, the latter the ex 'Claughton' fitting.) But whichever was adopted, it needed to be, firstly, fairly free-moving, and secondly, convenient to apply some force to if it did become stiff. I am afraid that the Riddles wheel satisfied neither condition. The theory was that the housewife stood in front of the mangle, the wheel end-on to her, and turned it with one hand while guiding the clothes in with the other. But did you ever see a housewife mangling (assuming that you were not too young, so that you were brought up in the washing machine/spin dryer age) *while sitting down*? So why should a driver have to stand up, if the reverser were stiff, to move it? The secret was to make it so that two hands could be brought to bear, with the shoulders behind them, and that was easily done with the normal LM type: if there were no stiffness, a half-turn was a one-handed job, unlocking, turning and relocking in one easy wrist movement. With the BR standard engines such a thing was just not on.

And then there were the controls for the ejectors and injectors, which were in constant use, and those for the train heating and the rest. The valves were all taken out of the cab, to cut down heat radiation for the crew. They all had to be operated by longish spindles coming through bushes in the cab front (which was inclined at 45° to avoid internal reflection at night) and steadied by guides in brackets fixed to the firebox backplate. Because of the risk of binding at these points, each spindle was solemnly given a universal joint, and that, plus the length of the spindles, made them so whippy and loose that you could seldom open the valves without brute force. All effort was dissipated before it got to the actual valve spindle. The whole concept was pretty crude.

Apart from these idiosyncrasies, however, there was a lot of very sound design in the whole range of standard engines, and they were remarkably free from the sort of weaknesses and deficiencies that have too often needed to be referred to hitherto in this book. In view of their design ancestry, perhaps this was not altogether surprising. From the depot maintenance angle, therefore, once the initial changes had been made, they presented few problems and were often a significant improvement on what had gone before.

I started looking at LM locomotives with the ubiquitous Class 5, and this makes a good starting point for the BR range also. There was great fundamental similarity between the standard engine and its Stanier predecessor, and yet in practice they were as unlike as chalk and cheese. The boiler was, apart from fittings, the latest LM Class 5 boiler with 28 superheater elements, but redraughted according to the Swindon formulae (which were held in high esteem by the Riddles team).

I had many, many runs on them on the Midland Division, notably on the Derby-Bristol road, and a few elsewhere. But after the real get-up-and-go enthusiasm and willingness of an LM Class 5, they were just not in the same category at all. For a start, they were as cold as the proverbial charity: the wonderful free steaming of the LM engine was nowhere to be found in this one. The pressure gauge was perpetually hanging back and no matter what firing technique was used — thick or medium fire, little-and-often or more every ten minutes — you were getting the firehole doors shut as quickly as possible to keep some heat in, and there was smoke at the chimney-top, and the crew were looking worried as she inevitably got down to about 170lb/sq in and stayed there until the regulator was shut again. At this sort of pressure a Standard Class 5 was pretty lame, weak as a kitten and getting nowhere at all.

Then again, they had that hard, rattly ride common to most of the standard engines, and that did nothing to endear them to their crews. So it would not be too strong to say that LM men regarded them with a healthy dislike, a feeling almost of being punished for some unknown offence by being given one instead of a Stanier Class 5.

On a note of somewhat black humour, however, on one occasion I saw one — No 73001 from Derby, I think — so grievously mismanaged that I was surprised she got as far as she did. The train was a relief from Derby to St Pancras, at Easter 1954, running in front of the 4.30pm from Manchester. I climbed on about 10min before departure, to find her simmering at about 220lb/sq in and with an immense, totally black fire piled right up to the top of the firehole under the smokeplate. Faint signs of smoke coming from somewhere within this 3ft thick bed of coal indicated that there was some fire down below. Not satisfied with this, the fireman prodded the top off the pile with his shovel and got some more in. As soon as we started this was the signal for more furious activity of the same kind. I looked at the driver, and he gave me a somewhat puzzled, pained look — it was not his regular mate — but said nothing.

As soon as we got away round the curve to Way & Works box, the pressure started to tumble. By Draycott it was down to 160, with the water nowhere near half glass, and still the fireman shovelled. I tried to discourage him, but to no avail. The driver then suggested that he ease up and for fully 60sec he put the shovel down. The fire looked appalling — there was still no flame through the coal under the door. We did not need to shut off for the slack round to Trent Junction, for we were not up to 60mph, pressure was down to 140lb/sq in and the large ejector was on to keep the brakes from dragging. Finally, at Kegworth, as we were rambling along at about 45-50, the driver put his foot down, and addressed his mate with the firm injunction: 'Put that bloody shovel down, and don't you dare pick it up again until I tell you to!' The fireman subsided, cowed. I got off at Leicester — we had dropped fully ten minutes to there — with the fire untouched: it was beginning to show some modest heat here and there, and the pressure recovered to 160lb/sq in during the station stop. It is my guess that the shovel stayed on the tender shovelling plate until somewhere about Kettering before anything more needed to be done. Do not suppose that I am suggesting that a Stanier Class 5 would have had anything but constipation from such treatment, but it would certainly not have succumbed to that extent.

Somehow the Scottish men seemed able to produce some quite fair results with them from time to time, though by no stretch of the imagination was their work ever superior to that of a Stanier engine, seldom even as good. They were not helped by the very heavy piston ring wear which continued to afflict them: at St Rollox shed it was normal, with engines working the Aberdeen and Inverness roads, to change piston rings at 11-12,000miles with the piston-valve engines and at 8,000miles

114

with the Caprottis. But about the best run I have been able to trace on the LM or Scottish Regions was with a Caprotti, No 73135, in the latter days of steam on the Glasgow-Aberdeen service when Class 5s had to work turn-and-turn about with A4s and seldom disgraced themselves in doing so. She had an eight-coach train of 255tons tare, and the fireworks were kept for the 32.5miles of racing ground from Perth to Forfar.*

An excellent climb was made to Stanley Junction, with 60 attained by Luncarty and no greater fall than to 57½ at Stanley, after a couple of miles at 1 in 125. Thereafter, 80½ was reached in the dip to the Tay viaduct, and after 76 at Cargill and 83½ on the 1¼ miles down to Coupar Angus, speed was held between 88 and 82 on the almost level road on to Forfar, reached in well under 'even time' in 30min 58sec. This was good work by any standards, but was distinctly untypical of a 73000.

Yet on the Rugby Testing Plant, after reducing the blastpipe orifice by ¼in (so much for the precision of Swindon's draughting design!) they managed to get boiler outputs from No 73008 which matched, or even slightly exceeded, what unaltered Stanier Class 5s had produced. And out on the road tests with the dynamometer car, No 73008 took a train far heavier than anything normally handled, augmented by electric dynamic braking from the Mobile Test Vehicles to the equivalent of 560tons, pass-to-pass Appleby to Ais Gill summit in 26min 55sec for the gruelling 17.5miles, an average speed of 39.0mph. If anything showed the disparity between test results and performance in normal service, that did!

The 'Britannias', by contrast, were very different machines. The big boiler was indefatigable, and relatively easy to fire once the technique of keeping the back corners of the firebox well filled had been mastered. They could be driven really hard without distress and produced some very fine results.

The troubles which they encountered on the Great Eastern section with water carry-over, broken piston heads and shifted coupled wheels had been overcome before the LM Region was seriously involved with them. Nevertheless, they were regarded by some men as somewhat inferior to the rebuilt 'Royal Scots', whose work they normally shared. The fact was that they could not be successfully handled in anything like the same way as a 'Scot' to get results, and men had to be educated, or learn, how to drive them to get value.

In the summer of 1954 I had occasion to visit Holyhead shed on business, and the five 'Britannias' Nos 70045-9 had been received there new only a few weeks before. I rode back to Crewe on the day 'Irish Mail' on No 70046, with a packed train of 15 bogies, about 470tons tare, and as we stood at the platform end, looked down on by the masts of *Cambria* just arrived from Dun Laoghaire, I asked the driver: 'Ever had one of

*See *Railway Magazine*, January 1964.

these engines before?' 'Only once up to now', he replied. 'How did you find her?' 'Oh, quite well, but I thought she seemed a bit sluggish getting away'. So I outlined the big boiler theory, and said: 'If you find she's like that, drop her down a bit more and flog her — the boiler will have no difficulty in coping with it'. For good measure I suggested that, rather than the 15% cutoff and often first valve of the regulator that he was used to with a 'Scot', he should reckon 20-25% as more normal for a 'Britannia', with the regulator wide open.

He took me very literally. We blasted up that horrible 1 in 85 off the platform end and past the shed in full gear and most of the regulator, sanders on continousuly, and then once over the top he proceeded to turn the reversing wheel — oh, so slowly — until by Rhosneigr she was still on about 30% and doing the best part of 70. We stormed up past Ty Croes like this and came down Bodorgan bank to touch 80 in the dip. The driver seemed satisfied with that and once we were clear of Bangor took things rather more easily, using full regulator with 22% cutoff to keep this heavy train rolling at a steady 72-75mph all the way to Mold Junction (apart from the Llandudno Junction slack and the Llysfaen hump, of course). Boiler pressure was rock-steady at 240lb/sq in, half a glass of water was held steady by intermittent use of the exhaust injector at less than half its full range, and a thin fire, fully 6in below the bottom of the firehole door except in the back corners, was maintained blinding white with little-and-often firing. We were into Chester 3min early, despite a severe signal check outside which all but brought us to a stand on the curve.

They were economical, too. I rode on No 70034 *Thomas Hardy* one afternoon on the (then) 2.20pm Manchester (London Road) to Euston, and with the Colne portion added at Stockport we had 14 on, 443tons tare. The West Coast timings were not very hard at that time, and while the Longsight driver's inclination was to use full regulator, the whole of the work after Stoke was done on 15-20% cutoff — short for a 'Britannia'. Point-to-point times were kept with commendable accuracy — we were seldom as much as a minute out all the way — and the water consumption from Stockport to Euston was no more than 4,600gallons, or 25.3gal/mile, equivalent to a coal consumption of about 33lb/mile.

You could usually rely on the senior Midland men to make whatever was possible of an engine, much more so than the LNW men. When the 'Britannias' went to the Midland main line around 1955, they were soon producing some really first-class running on a road that calls for bursts of high power in getting away from permanent speed restrictions, usually on severely adverse gradients, and the ability to run free and fast on the downhill stretches. No 70014 seems to have made a name for herself — if the *Iron Duke* can be referred to in the usual locomotive feminine — on this road, and as an illustration of a 'Britannia' brilliantly handled I can hardly do better than quote a run on the up 'Palatine' with this engine hauling a nine-coach formation of 304tons tare on 'XL' Limit timings,

99min for the 99.1 miles from Leicester to St Pancras. * *Iron Duke* cut the net time to 87½min, with an actual running time of 91min 4sec.

Some of the running on that trip set quite new standards, no doubt prompted by a 7½min late start. To go over Kibworth at 68, after 9miles continuously against the collar from the Leicester start, the last 1½ miles at 1 in 156/151, was a measure of what was to come. There followed 88 at East Langton, an acceleration to 62 at Desborough North (on 4miles of 1 in 132/133 after the Market Harborough slack), 87 before Glendon Junction, 60 over Sharnbrook summit after the Wellingborough slack, and a joyous 95 down the other side. So 6½min of the late start had been recouped by Bedford and things could be taken at a slightly less exhilarating pace. Even so, the train was taken over the top of the long rise to Leagrave, mainly at 1 in 202, at a minimum of 63mph, the 68.9miles to passing Luton being run in two seconds under 61½min. How very much in harmony were engine, crew and route to put up such a magnificent performance. Work of this standard was rarely, if ever, seen on the West Coast main line with the 'Britannias'.

I really hesitate to say very much about the odd man, No 71000 *Duke of Gloucester*, for I never had the opportunity to ride on him/her. I had some dealings with the engine while it was on the Swindon test plant, for she was suffering the most appalling piston ring wear. If I recall rightly, they were having to change rings at about 4000miles to get consistent results without piston leakage. The input of the atomised oil to the Caprotti cylinders was very badly positioned, to the point where oil put into the inlet valve chest was carried straight out again with the exhaust steam and up the blastpipe without reaching the pistons. This had to be altered before the tests could proceed.

No 71000 was a sort of stretched 'Britannia' so far as boiler and chassis were concerned, and the stretching pulled the boiler out of all proportion. She was J. F. Harrison's *magnum opus*, being designed at Derby with minimum consultation with the Riddles/Cox team. Her subsequent performance always struck me as a sort of retribution: soon after Freddie Harrison came to Derby from Doncaster as CME, he had a couple of days out on the line and made two trips on 'Duchesses' between Crewe and Carlisle. On his return, he came into our office and started a session of Mechanical Inspector-baiting. He had never (he averred) ridden on engines with such an appetite for coal, they were the miners' friends, Doncaster Pacifics were infinitely superior, etc etc. I may say that he got back as good as he gave, with due allowance for our relative positions, for there were no illusions amongst the Mechanical Inspectors that the 'Duchesses' were unbeatable.

Well, the 'Duke' needed a mine in the tender — and a pair of firemen would not have come amiss. The cylinders were thermally highly efficient, and the engine could be driven on extremely short cut-offs, but

*See *Railway Magazine*, September 1959.

the boiler could only be described as a disaster. Its maximum output was not quite as high as that of a 'Britannia', despite the double chimney, and the coal consumption was phenomenal. Above a certain amount, extra coal fired just went straight out of the other end without producing another pound of steam. How the Crewe North men hated that engine! On the night Perth sleeper from Euston, which they employed her on from Crewe, she would gobble the whole tender-full, 10tons plus, in those difficult 292miles, despite filling the firebox on the shed and re-coaling before coming off. She was soon relegated to the easier jobs, and even then she showed herself to be a coal-eater. Certainly no published runs in ordinary service show her as doing anything that a 'Duchess' would not have done with consummate ease.

The other class of big engines about which something needs to be said was the Class 9F 2-10-0. These were the most numerous of the standard classes, running to 251 locomotives, and really proved quite remarkable in their versatility in handling everything from heavy mineral workings to express passenger trains.

As is now well known, the heavy freight engine in the range was to be a 2-8-2, with the 'Britannia' boiler, cylinders and motion, and 5ft 3in wheels. It could hardly have failed to be a fine machine. But R. A. Riddles was not entirely happy about the concept, both as regards adhesion and brakepower. Derby drawing office had a look at possible arrangements for braking the rear pony truck and opined that it could not be done satisfactorily (even though others had managed equivalent installations.) Riddles therefore veered off towards a 2-10-0, bearing in mind his experience with the MoS 2-10-0s (which were happily trundling along the Glasgow-Carlisle main line on freight trains). This would clearly give better adhesion, and brake power for working loose-coupled freight, than the existing 2-8-0s of company design.

There were snags, however, and they concerned primarily the design of the boiler and firebox. Within the height available in the loading gauge, it was extremely difficult to get a firebox of adequate depth over the last two pairs of coupled wheels if these were to be adequate in diameter for fast freight work. The compromise reached was to use 5ft 0in wheels, but in consequence the boiler barrel had to be 4½in smaller at the firebox end than that of the 'Britannia', and to keep a reasonably balanced design the grate had to be reduced to 40.2sq ft instead of 42, and humped. The free gas area through the tube bank came down as a result from 6.79sq ft to 5.49sq ft. The ashpan could not be given any worthwhile inclination on the side slopes to the central hoppers, while clearing the trailing wheels, and it was therefore necessary to provide a pair of raking doors along the ashpan sides for use during disposal. More often than not these doors remained open in service and acted as additional dampers, making control of blowing off virtually impossible.

This lack of height at the rear end also affected the frame design. The depth of frame plate over the trailing horn gaps was very much less than usual, and it was necessary to rivet on a flitch plate in this zone to provide the necessary vertical bending strength. I was far from happy about this arrangement, and prophesied early fracturing problems. Happily, I was proved wrong.

As the design began to take firmer shape, I recollect that an exercise was done on the Southern Region to assess how the 2-10-0 would shape up on one contemplated working, trains of continental ferry vans from Dover to Bricklayers Arms, by comparison with the 2-8-2 alternative. Tractive effort/speed curves were produced for each, based on test results already coming forward for other classes and estimates of the boiler outputs. The starting tractive effort fo the 2-10-0 was some 10% higher, but clearly the boiler output, which would be the limiting factor at anything over about 20mph, had to be smaller because of the reduced key dimensions. The timing calculations were made, and they established that the 2-10-0 would be 10min slower than the 2-8-2 because the tractive effort curves crossed at about 35mph, the 2-8-2 thereafter being higher. Consternation! That was not the answer that was being sought for discussions with the Motive Power people. So the graphs were taken away, the 'facts' reappraised, and the whole represented in such a way that the two tractive effort curves no longer crossed. All mention of journey item on any specific working was judiciously omitted!

All this was a bit theoretical, however. Once the 2-10-0s appeared, they were excellent performers. I rode with them on several occasions on the Woodford-Annesley services, which were specifically tailored to use their characteristics to best advantage, and where a very high esprit-de-corps was maintained by tight operating. For instance, if the engine rang off the shed late at Annesley, it was sent back and the train cancelled: the crew then lost their mileage bonus for the day, which was a good incentive to come off to time. The 66mile journey took about 2½hr with the load, and a little less northbound with the empties, and the crew did an out-and-home working within their shift, though taking to a fresh engine to come back after a short meal break. On the long falling grades of the Great Central line, these trains — unbraked — would be hustled along at 45-50mph in clear weather, when the distant signals could be sighted some way off, and full regulator and 40-45% cutoff were the order of the day when climbing. No problems with steaming, either.

Another line on which they were in their element on freight was the Settle and Carlisle, and latterly they almost took it over. They were completely sure-footed. It was on this line that I first came to realise the incredibly smooth ride of a 2-10-0 at speed. They were remarkable — no sense of the reciprocating motion at all, and none of the rattle and solidarity of ride that marred so many of the BR standard engines. There was just no sensation of speed of the type normal with steam locomotives. This was what made them so useful on passenger work, in spite of their apparent unsuitability. There was at least one recorded case of one reaching 90 down from Stoke box towards Peterborough, but I doubt whether the driver realised just what he was doing, and they were not fitted with speedometers.

One week, three of them were transferred to Newton Heath for the Ancoats-Rowsley workings over the Peak. It so happened that we had a couple of Llandudno excursions to work on the following Sunday, and for some reason the running foreman felt it necessary to consult me about the power to be used; I told him to mark up two of the new arrivals for the jobs, and after some hesitancy he arranged to do so. Panic on Saturday morning: the two drivers concerned arrived at the office door as an irate deputation, demanding to know why I had had a pair of 'Austerities' allocated to them. When they realised that they were 2-10-0s and not 'Austerities', they calmed down and listened to what I told them about the engines. 'From the driving point of view, pretend you are on a Black Five and drive it the same way. Remember to make sure your fireman keeps the back corners well filled, otherwise a medium fire will do the trick nicely'. Dubiously, they made their way out, clearly convinced the boss was affected by the heat. But the smiles on Monday told their own tale. 'It was great, Guv'nor. We had no trouble at all, and along the North Wales coast I gave her just the first valve and 25%, and I reckon we did a steady 70 all the way. Can I have one next time?'

This was easy work, however. For those who would wish to have an impression of the work of 2-10-0s on passenger trains that made full demand of their capabilities, I cannot do better than recommend study of a book written by one who fired and drove them on the Somerset & Dorset — a line to tax the finest engines built.*

There was a bit of trouble with the regulators on them soon after they came into service, usually during slipping, and when it happened you could not close the thing. That was not calculated to make drivers happy, for that was just the time when it was particularly important to be able to do so. What was more, with that mangle-wheel reverser you could not quickly spin the engine into mid-gear to regain control as you could with a Stanier engine. The cause was traced to distortion on the valves, and this was remedied by fitting smaller valves, which, despite giving a degree of throttling, did not seem to effect performance in any way.

The only dismal chapter in the 2-10-0 saga was concerned with the ten Franco-Crosti-boilered engines. There were marginal fuel savings to be had from this boiler, though not enough for the fireman to notice the difference in service. They steamed a little less freely than the standard engines, perhaps, but were in no way like the standard Class 5s in this respect. What the crews disliked intensely were the dirty conditions in the cab from the very soft blast, which was insufficient to clear the smoke above the cab roof in many weather conditions. Some of it was sucked back into the cab, and the unfortunate crew could soon get as grimy as

*Mendips Engineman, by P.W. Smith. (Oxford Publishing Co 1972).

their mount. In addition, from the maintenance point of view the final smokebox and chimney had extremely short lives: their temperature was low enough, after a double extraction of heat from the flue gases, to reach the dewpoint regularly, resulting in vicious attack by dilute sulphuric acid, which quickly holed them.

Three of the 2-10-0s were fitted with Berkley mechanical stokers in 1958, and were allocated to Saltley with the Washwood Heath-Carlisle fitted freights in mind. These were worked via the Settle & Carlisle line, and were quite demanding jobs lasting about 7hr. Clearly, anything that made the fireman's job easier on such workings was to the good, even though the firemen themselves were relieved at Masborough and Skipton. But the real benefit of a stoker was the ability to burn smaller and poorer grades of coal satisfactorily. Perhaps the allocation and the selected jobs were not ideal for this purpose, for a big depot like Saltley, with mechanical coaling plant, could not segregate selected batches of coal to these stoker-fired engines, nor could the depots to which they worked. So one regularly saw the slightly comical situation of the tender being coaled in about three stages, a small gang of men getting into the bunker between times to break up the large lumps, because the stoker screw jibbed at crushing anything sizeable. The engine moves involved at a busy depot were enough to send the outside foreman hairless! The Berkley stoker, too, was perhaps not the rugged and proved machine that, for instance, the American 'Standard' stoker was.

I only rode with one of these engines once, on the 4.45pm Water Orton-Carlisle fully fitted freight. The fireman, who was by no means wet behind the ears, had considerable difficulty in adjusting the stoker jets to give him an even spread of coal over the grate, and was for ever fiddling with them. Even so, the fire got into a somewhat lumpy state, and several times he picked up his shovel and fed small amounts by hand to even it up — and that is an awkward job to do over the stoker table plate. There were a couple of brief interruptions by jamming of the feed screw, but these were readily cured by reversing the stoker engine and setting it forward again. It was quite clear that for such an experiment to produce the desired results the coal grading situation needed to be put right, and even more important, there was an evident need for the sort of fireman experience that comes with everyday stoker operation.

The last class that I want to refer to is the Class 4 tender engine. Now I can only wonder why this design was ever built, except to have something to put in the place of the GWR 'Manors', and there were enough of those available to serve the few weight-restricted lines that needed them. Mostly, and certainly in the case of the LM Region, they worked on lines with no such restriction, and Class 5s or Class 4 2-6-0s would have been at least as suitable and, in the case of the Class 5 at least, more versatile.

My only direct contact with them came with the five Southport engines. These took over duties which had been the prerogative of LM

Class 5s and 2-6-4 tanks, and a very poor job they made of it. Their steaming was decidedly erratic, and they seemed to have precious little life in them. After a lot of complaint, not only from the enginemen but also from the operating authorities as a result of lost time, it was arranged that No 75029, at that time the only one fitted with a double blastpipe and chimney, should be loaned from Oxford to Southport for trials. This would overcome the steaming trouble and that would be that.

I rode on her on the first day with a Motive Power Inspector, on the 12noon Manchester Victoria-Southport, stopping at Pendleton, Bolton, Wigan and St Lukes, with seven coaches, 234tons tare — well below the permitted load. The coal was Mosley Common Grade 2, loaded on at Southport, fair lump coal with very little slack in it, and the firing was carefully controlled, but the steaming was poor in the extreme. When running the main valve of the regulator was partly open, giving a steam chest pressure 50-60lb/sq in below that in the boiler. But before Bolton we were down to 175lb/sq in, using 30% cutoff, and with similar working on to Wigan we were all the time between 190 and 200 and quite unable to do better. Finally, on the near-level sprint thence to Southport we just managed to get up to 70mph at Bescar Lane, but by that time pressure was down to 155 and there was just an inch of water in the gauge glass. Water consumption for the 35miles was 1,400gal, or 40 gal/mile. This was a lot less than inspiring. They wrestled with the engine at Southport, including getting most of the superheater elements out because of blocked flues, but she was precious little better after all the work and was returned to Oxford quite unmourned.

I am told on good authority that the picture on the St Pancras-Bedford semi-fasts, which they took over from Compounds and the like, was very similar. Mechanically they were a lot better than the old Compounds, which by the 1950s were falling apart, but as operating tools they left a very great deal to be desired.

Such, then, was the impact of the BR standard locomotives as seen through LM Region eyes. If one were to summarise, it would be fair to say that two classes were generally welcome, the 'Britannias' (when men learned how to get the best out of them, which was not by pretending that they were 'Royal Scots') and the 2-10-0s. Two classes were heartily disliked, 71000 and the Class 5s, which dismally failed by comparison with the existing Regional equivalents. The Class 4 4-6-0s were reckoned to be poor tools, and the 2-6-4 tanks were inferior to the home product. The remainder were copies of the LMS designs, and no good purpose was seen in altering the original.

Not much of a reward for all the effort put into the design and construction of 999 locomotives of 12 types that were to carry BR on for the foreseeable future.

14/CME Unrecognised

It is a well-known fact that everyone knows how to do his superior's job better than the incumbent himself. The general public, too, when they make an infrequent journey by train, are clearly more adept at running a railway than those whose daily bread and butter depend on doing so, and are not afraid to speak their minds. It seems to me that I need no further excuse for presenting the chapter that follows.

In doing so, it must be borne in mind that any CME has to work hand in glove with Operating, Civil Engineering and (often at second hand) Commercial Departments, not omitting the Motive Power Department where this is separately identifiable, in producing power which will meet a specification for future requirements. Such a specification may be precise or woolly, and in some cases it may be a distillation of what can be readily provided, a sort of CME marketing exercise in what users may find tempting. Having satisfied the laid-down criteria, he is now in a position, jointly with other interested departmental chiefs, to go forward to his Board or other authority for financial approval to build. The very joint nature of the whole procedure, and the close scrutiny given all along the line, means that no modern CME has the ability and scope to indulge his independent fancies very far. His products have to match a visible traffic need.

By the same token, any railway which designs its own locomotives has, by the very nature of the people in the design organisation, a considerable measure of built-in continuity in the process: a recognisable design style emerges, and develops and changes very slowly, influenced only partly by the views of the CME himself and much more by the longevity of the end product and hard, practical considerations such as spares provision, etc. Standardisation extending over quite lengthy periods is essential, provided that it is not allowed to stultify development, as it tended to do on certain railways. Rarely indeed is the opportunity afforded to an R A Riddles to start with a clean piece of paper and produce a new, standardised range of locomotives.

And yet, as what has gone before has indicated, nobody in the CME organisation of the LM Region was in any way satisfied with the locomotive fleet that operated on the Region. I think it was probably true to say that the CME staff, and particularly the Mechanical Inspectors (who had a rather unique view of events very close to ground level), were at least as dissatisfied as the Motive Power people with the operating tools, if not more so. What follows, therefore, will be an attempt to look coolly and objectively at the LM Region's locomotive fleet in, say, 1948, on the assumption that traffic requirements were expressed in an imaginative and forward-looking way, and from that look, to produce a medium-term plan for adapting the locomotive fleet to fulfil those requirements well into the 1960s, be it by building new or by rebuilding of what was already available. It will take cognisance of national factors and trends beyond railway control which bore in on the operation of steam locomotives in the post-war years, and make due provision to deal with their effects. It will also seek to look at the requirements through the eyes of an established Chief Locomotive Draughtsman at Derby and follow the sort of overall approach which had evolved in 1948 in new locomotive design.

What were the external influences? Firstly, fuel trends must be recognised. The steady expansion of mechanised coal mining in Britain was producing coal of an inherent quality not greatly different from that available before the war, but average size was falling and as a result, increasing quantities had to be made into briquettes and ovoids to make it suitable for other than pulverised fuel or chain-grate firing in static installations. (It was somewhat ironical that, as this supply situation was developing, the railways should have gone more and more to hoisting coal up into high bunkers and dropping it thence into tenders, still further degrading the quality by breakage).

Now the steam locomotive, with its high combustion rates under strong induced draught to obtain the necessary heat release rates in a space confined by loading gauge restrictions, could only exist on a diet of large coal, or by mechanised firing. A fire maintained by hand, with sufficient thickness to sustain the inevitable unevenness which this method produced, would soon get constipated if sufficient primary air could not be passed through it, and this called for a highly porous bed which only medium to large coal — say 2in and over — could provide.

Alternatively, a mechanical stoker could be adjusted to maintain a thin fire of quite uniform thickness and texture, and clearly this could pass the necessary air for combustion readily, even if smaller coal were used: the draught would, if needed, keep the bed almost fluidised, though at the expense of a greater degree of unburnt fuel loss up the chimney. And what actively inhibited the use of mechanical stokers in Britain in the late 1940s and 1950s was the fact that NCB pricing policy did not recognise the need to discount the purchase price of small, inferior coals sufficiently to offset the costs associated with supply and maintenance of a mechanical stoker and the extra 10% consumption, or thereabouts, arising from firing such coal in locomotives. In parallel, the oil/coal price differential was too great to justify a changeover to oil fuel. But there was nothing in the work demanded which required the firing rates that a stoker could give.

The other major factor was the labour situation. Full employment, save only in some regional pockets of under-development, produced difficult recruiting situations for railways. It was not primarily a question of rates of pay, but rather of conditions of service: shift work, often highly irregular: physically taxing work under bad, even in some cases degrading conditions: exposure to weather in all its extremes: dirt: the effect on social life and activities. The straight 8-to-5 job in a comfortably warm factory with a tea trolley was often too tempting. So, with the best will in the world towards improving facilities, the railways were never again likely to get staff for such work as cleaning, firedropping, even for firing, in the numbers or of the quality to which they had been accustomed.

The footplate had always been a somewhat crude environment, compounded of noise, dirt, vibration and violent movement. There were extremes of burning heat and cold draughts, and few things could be achieved without substantial physical effort. Superimposed on all this were often nonsenses that further depreciated the standards of the workplace: one thinks, for instance, of the Midland regulator handles, or the propensity of the cab roof joint on the 'Royal Scots' to drip rainwater down the driver's neck when he was seated, or the joys of turning a red-hot pricker round through 180° to get it from firebox to fire-iron tunnel. Less and less were footplate staff prepared, as their forebears had been prepared, to accept such nonsenses when they could see perfectly straightforward ways of avoiding such conditions and/or dangers.

Further, the time could hardly be long delayed when the alternatives to steam had to be seriously tackled. Clearly the biggest dividend would come from electrification of intensive suburban services, the Tilbury line being perhaps the prime example. In addition, the branch line problem, in so far as it remained at all, had to be tackled by some form of self-contained diesel passenger vehicle, and for main lines diesel traction had to be produced in small numbers and undergo a prolonged development period before widespread adoption could be contemplated. It could be foreseen that such moves would throw up large numbers of the older and less adaptable locomotives, initially among tank locomotives of all sizes and superannuated main line power, and thereafter make inroads into the larger and more modern portion of the locomotive fleet.

So in order to meet the more and more strenuous traffic demands, particularly in the passenger field but also to some degree with continuous-braked freight trains — to a level which came to exceed prewar levels of performance — and under worsening external influences it was necessary to move progressively towards:

Large boilers and fireboxes, to allow combustion of less suitable coals at lower unit rates on the grate and with lower standards of skill on the part of the fireman.
Use of mechanical stokers where performance levels required the

feeding of coal at rates much in excess of about 3,000lb/hr with any regularity or continuity.

The use of two cylinders wherever possible, outside the frames, to facilitate preparation and maintenance.

The use of rocking grates, hopper ashpans, self-cleaning smoke-boxes and other recent developments to take as much unpleasantness and hard labour as possible out of disposal work.

Provision of comfortable cabs with good weather protection (often for running in both directions) and working conditions.

In support of locomotives meeting these criteria, too, some real improvements in depot facilities for both servicing and maintenance were badly needed. Was it really necessary, for instance, for firemen to carry buckets of dry sand over long distances to refill sandboxes, when perfectly good systems of overhead storage and dispensing by hose were available?

Let us, therefore, make a critical stocktaking of the more modern element of the LM Region locomotive fleet to see how far it met these requirements and was basically competent: many of their deficiencies have been referred to in the appropriate chapters which have gone before. It may be convenient to take the classes in engine numerical order.

40001-40070 Fowler Cl. 3MT 2-6-2 tank (Chapter 11). Performance very poor. Required to be superseded early by alternative forms of traction. Little material suitable for salvage for rebuilding except perhaps coupled wheels and bissel trucks.

40071-40209 Stanier Cl. 3MT 2-6-2 tanks (Chapter 11). Performance poor. Further rebuilding with 6B boiler not warranted with prospect of being superseded early by alternative forms of traction. Some material salvageable.

40563-40700 Fowler Cl. 2P 4-4-0 tender (Chapter 4). Performance poor. Rebuilding not justified by future traffic requirements. No material salvageable except tender.

40900-40939, 41045-41199 Fowler Cl.4P compound 4-4-0 tender (Chapter 4). Performance reasonable, but mechanically unsatisfactory. Rebuilding of a proportion probably justified for main line secondary work, assisting, etc. Boiler, wheels, tender and some other material salvageable for partial rebuild.

41200-41209 Ivatt Cl.2MT 2-6-2 tank (Chapters 7, 11). Performance good. No further work needed. Suitable for further building, subject to traffic requirements.

42187-42299, 42673-42699. Fairburn Cl. 4MT 2-6-4 tank (Chapter 11). Performance good. Little further work needed. Suitable for further building, subject to traffic requirements.

42300-42424 Fowler Cl. 4MT 2-6-4 tank (Chapter 11). Performance good, but some mechanical weaknesses to overcome. Suitable for retention to extent dictated by traffic requirements, or for rebuilding as 2-6-0 tender engine.

42500-42536 Stanier C1. 4MT 3-cyl 2-6-4 tank (Chapter 11). Performance good. Mechanically fairly satisfactory, but third cylinder increased maintenance costs. Suitable for retention to extent dictated by traffic requirements. Further rebuilding not warranted with prospect of being superseded early by alternative forms of traction. Some salvageable material — coupled wheels and axleboxes, bissel trucks, bogies, frame components, fittings, etc — for rebuilding.

42700-42944 Fowler C1. 6P5F 2-6-0 tender (Chapter 7). Performance good. Mechanically fairly satisfactory, but some weaknesses to overcome. Suitable for retention to extent dictated by traffic requirements.

42945-42984 Stanier C1. 6P5F 2-6-0 tender (Chapter 11). Performance fair. Mechanically fairly satisfactory, but some weaknesses to overcome. Suitable for short-term retention. Some salvageable material — coupled wheels and axleboxes, bissel trucks, frame components, tender, fittings, etc — for rebuilding.

43000-onwards Ivatt C1. 4MT 2-6-0 tender (Chapter 7). Performance good after draughting modifications. Suitable for further building, subject to traffic requirements.

44027-44606 Fowler C1. 4F 0-6-0 tender (Chapter 4). Performance fair, but mechanically not satisfactory. Boilers, wheels, tender and much other material salvageable for partial rebuild.

44758-45499 Stanier C1. 5MT 4-6-0 tender (Chapter 6). Performance good. Mechanically good after frame modifications. Suitable for retention to extent dictated by traffic requirements, but early engines with thin frames offer scope for more radical rebuilding, with most material salvageable.

45500-45551 Fowler C1. 6P 4-6-0 tender (Chapter 8). Performance fair. Mechanically fair, and boilers well towards life expiry. Suitable for rebuilding (except 45500-45511) to Class 7P using coupled wheels, bogie, motion and other components.

45552-45742 Stanier C1. 6P 4-6-0 tender (Chapter 8). Performance good, but not really adequate for traffic demand. Mechanically sound. Much material salvageable for rebuilding — bogie, coupled wheels, outside cylinders, motion, frame components, fittings, cab, etc.

46100-46170 Stanier rebuilt C1. 7P 4-6-0 tender (Chapter 12). Performance good. Mechanically sound. Remaining parallel-boiler engines in process of rebuilding with 2A boiler.

46200-46212 Stanier C1. 7P 4-6-2 tender (Chapter 9). Performance good, but could be improved. Mechanically fairly good, but some weaknesses to be overcome. Suitable for modest rebuilding to achieve full life of boiler.

46220-46257 Stanier C1. 8P 4-6-2 tender (Chapter 9). Performance very good. Mechanically good, but some weaknesses to be overcome. Suitable for rebuilding with mechanical stoker to achieve full potential.

46400-46419 Ivatt C1. 2MT 2-6-0 tender (Chapter 7). Performance good. No further work needed. Suitable for further building, subject to traffic requirements.

47000-47004 Kitson C1. OF 0-4-0 tanks; 47160-47169 Fowler C1. 2F 0-6-0 tanks; 47260-47681 Fowler C1. 3F 0-6-0 tanks. Mechanically fair. Suitable for experimental rebuilding to achieve better mechanical endurance.

47967-47999 Fowler Garratt 2-6-0 + 0-6-2 (Chapter 10). Performance fair. Mechanically bad. Unsuitable for retention.

48000-48772 Stanier C1. 8F 2-8-0 tender (Chapter 10). Performance good. Mechanically good, could be improved by frame modifications. Suitable for retention.

49500-49674 Fowler C1. 7F 0-8-0 tender (Chapter 10) Performance good. Mechanically poor. Unsuitable for rebuilding. Suitable for retention only until traffic requirements permit withdrawal.

Having taken stock of the more modern element — something like half — of the locomotive fleet, we need to look at the traffic needs of the railway. There is evidence that the LM operators were very slow to realise that the passenger fleet of the numbers and power range that existed was not going to meet requirements of increased speeds, heavier trains and a deteriorating coal situation in the 1950s, for which the only palliative would be an undesirable degree of double-heading. In the freight field, while the loose-coupled mineral traffic could in general be satisfactorily handled by the 2-8-0s, the expanding fitted freight situation was less well covered: the preoccupation with Class 5 4-6-0s was limiting loads to about 35 wagons, and less on heavy roads.

There were, within these generalisations, more specific problems. The West Coast main line was undoubtedly one. South of Carnforth the 'Duchesses' were in their element, and their performance was only dependent on what their crew was prepared to put into the pot. But once into the fell country and across the border into Scotland, other factors came into play, of a random nature, which could upset service reliability. Of these, adhesion was a major one, and water capacity was another. A drizzle on Beattock, early morning dew, or falling autumn leaves on Grayrigg, and any Pacific could be struggling to keep her feet and the train on the move. The 66miles of 'waterless' country from Mossband troughs to Strawfrank troughs (73 from Carlisle, if Mossband happened to be 'out') were distinctly worrying to many men, and it needed little persuasion for them to stop at Beattock Station for a quick 1,000gallons to be on the safe side — even though most such decisions proved to be wrong in the event. And it must not be forgotten that the Liverpool/Manchester-Glasgow trains were struggling with 'Jubilees' on 'limited load' timings, and a fair amount of assistance between Preston and Carlisle was being required.

Then there were lines like the Midland main line, where Class 5s and 'Jubilees' reigned supreme until the late 1950s. The running was of a very high order, but the limit of 300tons (or nine coaches) for a 'Jubilee' on 'XL limit' timings led to an increasing amount of double-heading. A lot of sustained boiler power was needed on the longer banks, notably from Bedford up to Leagreave, coming towards the end of a longish run, and with some grades of coal, the fire on a 'Jubilee' was hardly in the best condition to supply it.

A perennial stimulus to bright ideas was the Highland main line between Perth and Inverness, where the Class 5s, in effect, did it all. They were limited to 255tons, and while that got by for most of the year on the passenger work, the 'Royal Highlander' invariably required two of them, and wistful eyes were directed towards Garratts to do the job single-handed. Some of the strengthened summer trains, too, were beyond the capability of a single Class 5 and running speeds could have been substantially improved with faster climbing.

In contrast to all this, the running of summer weekend excursions — extremely numerous at that period — caused many a Shedmaster to develop ulcers: everything that was fitted with vacuum brakes, suitable or not, was pressed into reluctant service. Class 4F 0-6-0s staggered over the Peak from the East Midlands to Blackpool with 10 corridors: 'Austerities' did the same from Manchester and attempted to run at 60 over the level road from Preston to Blackpool North. S&D 2-8-0s were pressed into attempting the same sort of thing southwards out of Bath. There were just not enough mixed traffic tender engines of suitable characteristics to meet the demand, and the 2-6-4 tanks, capable as they were, could not wholly fill the bill because of water capacity limitations, although on Saturdays they were available in fair numbers.

My proposals, therefore, within the guidelines set out earlier in this chapter, would have been as follows:

(a) To split the operation of the West Coast main line, for locomotive purposes, at the most appropriate division point, namely Preston, and
— confine the 'Duchesses' south of Preston, modifying them, with mechanical stokers, to develop their maximum potential;
— produce a new design for running north of Preston, stoker-fired, improved adhesion and water capacity, ie a Garratt.
(b) To rebuild the 'Jubilees' as Pacifics, thus giving them the boiler power to meet postwar conditions of coal and firing aptitude.
(c) To venture into the 2-8-2 field, on a fully mixed traffic basis, both for main line fitted freight work and for lines such as the Highland and to Oban.
(d) To produce a heavy-duty 2-8-4 tank engine for certain steeply graded, frequent-stop lines carrying heavy commuter traffic requiring

better adhesion and acceleration than the 2-6-4 tanks could produce.

(e) To convert numbers of 2-6-4 tanks into 2-6-0 tender engines, in the wake of electrification of the LTS and gradual dieselisation of other lines, to make them more versatile for weekday freight and weekend excursion work.

(f) To make improvements to other basically sound designs to fit them for a further 10-20 years of more intensively-used work.

(g) To scrap ruthlessly the less satisfactory designs, using material from them where suitable for the rebuilding programme.

All this presupposes that developments on the railway network in the 1950s — the gradual decline in mined coal tonnage and in general merchandise traffic, growth of block train working and reduction in local freight trips, the steady closure of rural branch lines and the use of heavier main-line coaching stock at improved speeds — continued along broadly similar lines to what did in fact happen, and that improved scheduling and locomotive diagramming techniques allowed the workload to be encompassed with fewer locomotives. In all conscience there was scope for it: I had a 'Crab' turn in 1957 at Newton Heath, for which the engine was solemnly prepared — an hour's work for driver and fireman — and ran a total of 7miles between Brewery Sidings and Brindle Heath before coming back on to the shed, 6hr later, to be fully disposed again!

Now all this would have caused a pretty heavy load on the main works — enough, perhaps, to justify turning over whole erecting shop bays at Crewe and Derby to major rebuilding only — though much of the erecting shop work would have been needed in any case. It would also have been fairly costly, even though it could be expected to produce substantial net revenue betterment due to the commercial acceptibility of higher speeds, the running of larger and fewer freight trains, and the reduction in double-heading, quite apart from a fall in delay, improved timekeeping, and widespread reduction in the amount of depot maintenance work required.

It would therefore have been necessary to lay down a carefully integrated programme: at the design stage, to ensure the maximum possible reuse of suitable serviceable components from broken-up locomotives in the new designs, and the maximum use of standard components such as cylinders, axleboxes, etc, where the existing ones were unsuitable: and in the works, to ensure a regulated flow of locomotives for withdrawal to match the production of the rebuilds with salvageable components. But under suitable overall control such an integrated programme could have been achieved with minimal effect on the 'In and awaiting Works' element of the overall locomotive availability.

If you go along with me on the general proposition, let us have a more detailed look at the individual designs which would result.

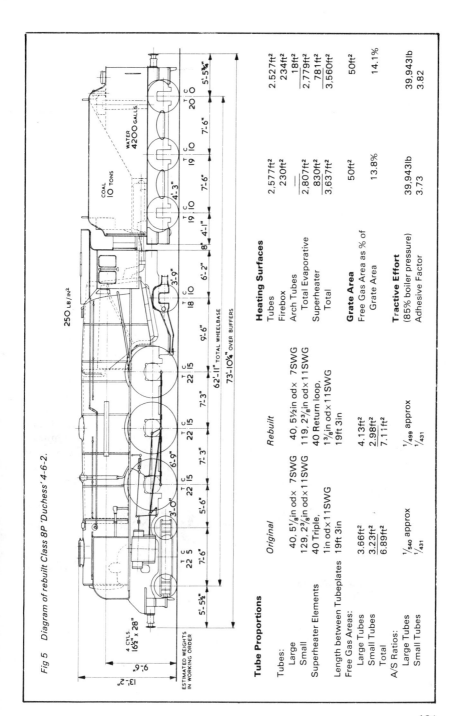

Fig 5   Diagram of rebuilt Class 8P 'Duchess' 4-6-2.

250 LB/IN²

4 CYLS.
16½" × 28"

ESTIMATED WEIGHTS
IN WORKING ORDER

WATER 4200 GALLS.

COAL
10 TONS

	T C	T C	T C	T C	T C	T C	T C	T C	T C	T C	T C
	22 5	22 15	22 15	22 15	18 10	19 10	19 10	20 0			

5'-5¼"   7'-6"   3'-0"   6'-9"   7'-3"   7'-3"   9'-6"   3'-9"   6'-2"   8' 4'-1"   7'-6"   7'-6"   5'-5¼"

62'-11" TOTAL WHEELBASE
73'-10¼" OVER BUFFERS

9'-6"
13'-2⅝"

Heating Surfaces

Tubes	2,527ft²
Firebox	234ft²
Arch Tubes	18ft²
Total Evaporative	2,779ft²
Superheater	781ft²
Total	3,560ft²

Grate Area

	50ft²
Free Gas Area as % of	
Grate Area	14.1%

Tractive Effort

(85% boiler pressure)	39,943lb
Adhesive Factor	3.82

Tube Proportions

	Original	*Rebuilt*
Tubes:		
Large	40, 5⅛in od× 7SWG	40, 5½in od× 7SWG
Small	129, 2³⁄₈in od×11SWG	119, 2³⁄₈in od×11SWG
Superheater Elements	40 Triple,	40 Return loop,
	1in od×11SWG	1⅜in od×11SWG
Length between Tubeplates	19ft 3in	19ft 3in
Free Gas Areas:		
Large Tubes	3.66ft²	4.13ft²
Small Tubes	3.23ft²	2.98ft²
Total	6.89ft²	7.11ft²
A/S Ratios:		
Large Tubes	1/540 approx	1/499 approx
Small Tubes	1/431	1/431

Heating Surfaces (Rebuilt)

Tubes	2,577ft²
Firebox	230ft²
Arch Tubes	—
Total Evaporative	2,807ft²
Superheater	830ft²
Total	3,637ft²

Grate Area (Rebuilt)

	50ft²
Free Gas Area as % of	
Grate Area	13.8%

Tractive Effort (Rebuilt)

(85% boiler pressure)	39,943lb
Adhesive Factor	3.73

The 'Duchesses': (46220-46257)

The generally accepted criterion for the capacity of a fireman was that he could shovel 3,000lb/hr of coal on a fairly continuous basis. With a 'Duchess' that meant a steam consumption, with exhaust steam injector in use, of about 25,000lb/hr. This was not much more than half of what the boiler *could* produce, given an adequate coal supply, and well out of any normal range of liability to slipping except at low speeds. With a mechanical stoker taking the back-breaking labour away from the fireman, the output for timing purposes could have been stepped up to a steam rate of, say, 34,000lb/hr, which still only represented about 75% of maximum and would have given a substantial reserve of power to cover variability of locomotive, fireman and coal. At such an output, which could have been called upon reliably at over about 25mph, the coal rate would have been about 5,000lb/hr, allowing for the additional 10% consumption with stoker firing.*

Between Euston and Preston, at this rate of output with the 'XL Limit' load of 510tons tare, the calculated start-to-stop timing which would be produced is a few seconds over 187min, and this is presented in more detail in Table 1. With a 4% recovery margin, a workable time to put in the timetable would have been 195min, representing an average speed of 64.4mph. (It should be remembered that this is based on the speeds permitted on the West Coast main line in the early 1950s, which were very different in some areas from those of the electric railway of today — 45 through Rugby to the Trent Valley line, 55 through Weaver Junction and 50 at both Warrington and Wigan, for example. The overall coal consumption for the 209.1 miles would be about 7tons. Maximum water consumption between troughs (assuming the worst case with one set of troughs out for repair) would have been about 3,100gallons. Accordingly, a six-wheeled tender with capacity for 10tons of coal and 4,200gallons of water would have sufficed, and would also have covered workings to Liverpool, Manchester and Chester with ease: no renewal of 70ft turntables would have been necessary.

For intensive use and such high performance, certain other modifications would also have been necessary, or at least desirable. These were:

(1) The use of arch tubes in the firebox, primarily for the purpose of supporting a more mechanically-sound brick arch.
(2) Modification of the back end frames, rear bissel truck and ashpan

Table 1. Euston-Preston

Locomotive:	Rebuilt 4-6-2 'Duchess' with mechanical stoker.
	Steam rate — 34,000lb/h with exhaust injector.
Load:	510 tons tare, 550 tons gross.

*See the author's contribution to *The LMS Duchesses*, ed. D. Doherty. (MAP 1973).

Distance		Running Time m. s.	Speeds mph
0.0	EUSTON	0.00	—
1.1	Camden No 1	—	25
5.4	Willesden Junc	8.53	—
7.0	Mp7	—	62½
14.2	Mp14¼	—	64½
17.5	Watford Junc	20.14	70½
31.7	Tring	32.37	66¼
40.2	Leighton Buzzard	—	84/80*
46.7	Bletchley	43.59	82/80½
52.4	Wolverton	—	83/80*
59.9	Roade	54.21	70½
62.8	Blisworth	56.48	78
69.7	Weedon	62.27	77/78
76.6	Kilsby Tunnel South	—	71½
82.6	RUGBY	73.17	80/45*
91.4	Shilton	—	69/68
97.1	Nuneaton	86.46	81½
102.3	Atherstone	—	78½/70*
110.0	Tamworth	96.25	82
116.3	Lichfield	101.48	74
124.3	Rugeley	108.02	79/77½
129.5	Milford	112.16	78½/76/77
133.6	STAFFORD	115.50	60*
138.9	Norton Bridge	120.43	68½
147.6	Whitmore	128.09	70/69
153.3	Betley Road	—	86½
158.1	CREWE	136.07	20*
160.9	Coppenhall Junc	140.32	53
166.9	Winsford Junc	145.48	72½
174.4	Weaver Junc	152.05	78/55*
180.2	Acton Grange Junc	157.48	73½/70
182.2	Warrington	159.37	50*
185.6	Winwick Junc	163.03	63
—	Golborne Junc	—	60½
192.6	Springs Branch No 1	169.39	70
193.8	Wigan NW	170.58	50*/53
197.1	Standish Junc	174.48	48/52½
—	Coppull	—	54/53
203.6	Euxton Junc	180.43	77½/76½/78
209.1	PRESTON	186.39	—

* Permanent speed restriction

along the lines of the arrangement on Nos 46256/7, to give better ashpan capacity and more reliable cleaning.

(3) The fitting of a multiple-valve regulator on the superheat side of the superheater header, to give better control.

(4) The fitting of roller bearing axleboxes throughout.

(5) The fitting of roller bearing big ends.

(6) An altered tube layout to permit the use of 5½in diameter superheater flues, giving slightly better free gas areas and much higher superheat temperatures.

(7) The fitting of a power-operated water scoop.

(8) Modifications to firebox to provide a flat grate to suit the mechanical stoker.

(9) Improvements to cab layout for crew comfort and convenience.

The diagram in Fig 5 shows the super-'Duchess', together with all the important dimensions and ratios, while Fig 6 shows the tubeplate layouts. The improved A/S ratios of the superheater flues, and the marginal improvement in total free gas area as a result, will be noted. A slight increase in coupled axle-load can be envisaged as a result of the use of roller bearings, etc, but this could be compensated by a reduction

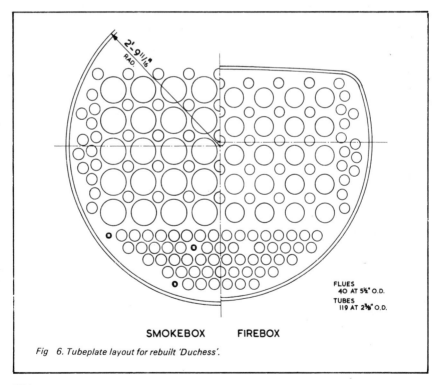

FLUES
40 AT 5½" O.D.
TUBES
119 AT 2⅜" O.D.

SMOKEBOX   FIREBOX

Fig 6. Tubeplate layout for rebuilt 'Duchess'.

in the percentage of reciprocating balance from the existing 50% to satisfy the Civil Engineer.

'Garratts' for North of Preston

North of Carnforth, the West Coast Main Line and its Scottish extension to Perth are severely graded, and abound in curvature preventing really fast, uninhibited running. Weather conditions adversely affect adhesion in critical areas of climbing. To meet these challenges, together with the paucity of water troughs north of the border, and provide adequate boiler power for sustained hard running beyond the capacity of a fireman to feed manually, there were only two possible approaches: either a 4-8-2 or an articulated locomotive.

The 4-8-2 approach must be rejected. Within the British loading gauge (and particularly that on the Caledonian section) the accommodation of a satisfactory boiler, even with coupled wheels of, say, 6ft 0in dia. would have been particularly difficult while giving a satisfactory fire-box/ashpan layout, reasonable tube proportions and a good front end layout and weight distribution. Further, its length, allied with the need for a four-axle tender to deal with the 242miles from Preston to Perth and the long intervals between troughs (and after Strawfrank there was nothing other than water columns) would have made even 75ft turntables barely adequate.

The natural choice would therefore have been a Garratt, and the clear choice of wheel arrangement would have been a 4-6-2 + 2-6-4, with two two-cylinder engines. And what better to base each engine on than the Class 5 4-6-0? A pressure of 225lb/sq in would give a tractive effort of slightly over 50,000lb, but an adhesion weight of about 114tons (only coming down about 25tons with use of fuel and water) would have been available through which to apply it, making it infinitely more sure-footed under difficult conditions than a 'Duchess'. Furthermore, a large, deep firebox, ideal for stoker firing at high burning rates, could have been provided in conjunction with a large short boiler barrel giving large free gas areas and good tube proportions. Riding would have been excellent, and crew conditions good.

To me, a natural starting point would have been the early Class 5s with 1in frames, Nos 45000-45069. There was a lot of good material in these which could have been used for the Garratts, given a requirement for new frame plates anyway (of greater thickness) to suit the 4-6-2 layout at a shorter wheelbase. The boilers (early domeless with straight throatplates and 27.8sq ft grates) could have been used elsewhere, as we shall see later.

The heart of any Garratt is, of course, the boiler: an appraisal of the work required, with particular reference to the heavy night sleeping car trains, suggests thinking in terms of a boiler output of 36,000lb/hr of steam for timing purposes, which with stoker firing would need supplying coal at something like 5,500lb/hr. This would justify a grate

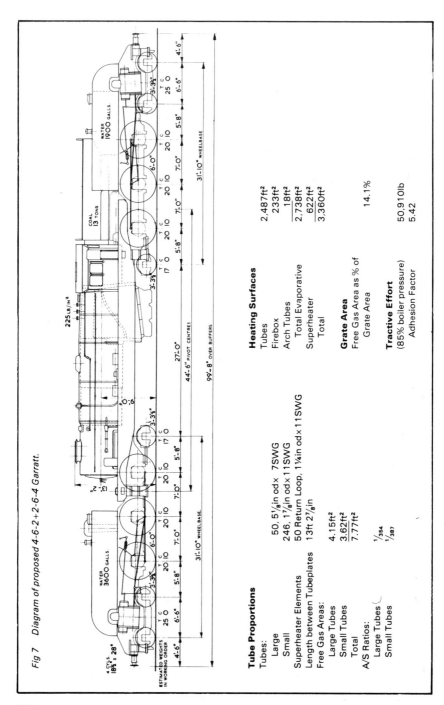

Fig 7   Diagram of proposed 4-6-2+2-6-4 Garratt.

Tube Proportions

Tubes:

Large	50, 5 1/8 in od × 7SWG
Small	246, 1 7/8 in od × 11SWG
Superheater Elements	50 Return Loop, 1 1/4 in od × 11SWG
Length between Tubeplates	13ft 2 7/8 in

Free Gas Areas:

Large Tubes	4.15ft²
Small Tubes	3.62ft²
Total	7.77ft²

A/S Ratios:

Large Tubes	1/364
Small Tubes	1/387

Heating Surfaces

Tubes	2,487ft²
Firebox	233ft²
Arch Tubes	18ft²
Total Evaporative	2,738ft²
Superheater	622ft²
Total	3,360ft²

Grate Area

Free Gas Area as % of Grate Area	14.1%

Tractive Effort

(85% boiler pressure)	50,910lb
Adhesion Factor	5.42

area of 55sq ft to keep the combustion rate down to 100lb/sq ft hr, which is essential to keep the unburnt fuel loss within bounds. This in turn demanded a free gas area through the tubes of about 8sq ft which could be provided by a barrel about 6ft 9in diameter with a distance between tubeplates no more than 13ft 3in. Standard tubes and flues could then be used. Fig 8 shows the tubeplate layouts with round-topped firebox.

For the Preston-Perth run a coal bunker capacity of about 13tons would be needed, while to bridge that Carlisle-Strawfrank gap in water supplies a tank capacity of about 5,500gallons would have been no more than necessary for comfort. The use of a mechanical stoker would have avoided the need for any form of rotary bunker and would have enabled the cab to be made weatherproof even when running bunker first.

So there is our high-speed heavy duty Garratt, using the existing cylinders, motion, bogie, coupled wheels and many frame components of a pair of early Class 5s. The inner bissel trucks, too, would have been salvaged from cut-up tank locomotives, only the radial arm needing alteration for length. Roller bearings would have been used on all axles. Centre frame, boiler and all tanks, bunker, cab, etc, would have been new. Full advantage would have been taken of the Beyer Peacock features which had been proved on Garratts in overseas service, notably

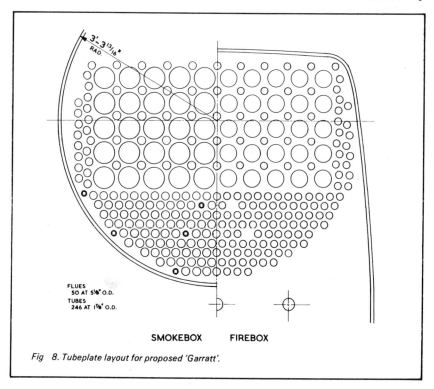

FLUES
50 AT 5⅛" O.D.
TUBES
246 AT 1⅞" O.D.

SMOKEBOX   FIREBOX

Fig 8. Tubeplate layout for proposed 'Garratt'.

the self-adjusting pivot centres and the power reverse gear, together with a multiple-valve regulator on the superheat side of the header and a double chimney.

A diagram of the beast is shown in Fig 7 with relevant dimensions. No question of turning normally arises, but it so happens that facilities for doing so were available on triangles at Preston, Carlisle and Glasgow anyway, if required for tyre wear equalisation, etc: no such facility existed at Perth.

At a steam rate of 36,000lb/hr, performance would have been impressive, to say the least. Again using the 510ton train that our stoker-fired 'Duchess' had brought into Preston from Euston, the calculated Garratt performance thence to Glasgow, with Carlisle and Motherwell stops only, is set out in Table 2. Again using a 4% recovery allowance, the Preston-Carlisle, Carlisle-Motherwell and Motherwell-Glasgow Central timings would reasonably have been 93½, 95 and 17½min respectively. With 7 min for the Preston engine change, 3min at Carlisle and 2 min at Motherwell, the overall Euston-Glasgow timing on this basis would thus have amounted to 412min this gives an average speed, stops included, of 58.5mph.

The 'Princesses' (46200-46212)

Just to finish off the Class 8P engines, one must say something about these 12 engines, which could be ill spared — the number of high-powered engines was too small for that — yet could hardly fit into the emerging West Coast working pattern. But another route badly needed locomotives of greater power if the passenger work was to be accelerated and some double-heading avoided: I refer to the Settle and Carlisle, together with the extension over the G. & S.W. route to Glasgow. The 'Princesses', suitably modified but retaining hand firing, would have been suitable for this, and in these numbers could have taken over the whole of the Class 1 passenger work and the faster freight jobs.

To make a real job of the 'Princesses', however, considerable modification was necessary. As it happened, the ill-fated No 46202 *Princess Anne* pointed the way, with what was largely the cylinders, motion and front end generally of a 'Duchess' grafted on to the 'Princess' chassis. But this rebuild was not taken far enough; further work was necessary if full advantage was to be taken of the locomotive.

The boiler, as indicated in Chapter 9, was a bit of a problem, because the barrel diameter was hardly adequate to match the grate. But making a new tube layout to suit 5½in diameter flues within the existing boiler with combustion chamber firebox, could result in a slight increase in free gas area, which would have been beneficial. In conjunction with a double blastpipe and chimney, that would have made steaming more reliably satisfactory and at the same time given higher superheat and thus better cylinder efficiency, particularly when worked hard. The fitting of arch tubes to support the brick arch would have completed the boiler.

Table 2. Preston-Glasgow

Locomotive: New 4-6-2 + 2-6-4 Garratt with mechanical stoker.
Steam rate — 36,000lb/h.
Load: 510 tons tare, 550 tons gross.

Distance		Running Time m. s.	Speeds mph
0.0	PRESTON	0.00	—
1.3	Oxheys	3.39	37
9.5	Garstang	12.36	68
21.0	Lancaster	22.23	74/60*
27.3	Carnforth	28.01	73½
30.5	Mp9½	—	63
34.6	Milnthorpe	—	71
40.1	Oxenholme	39.52	54½
45.0	Mp24	—	47
47.2	Grayrigg	—	43
53.2	Tebay	54.46	68
58.7	Shap Summit	61.45	35
72.2	Penrith	74.47	68/60*/70/60*
77.0	Plumpton	79.03	75½
—	Wreay	—	80/70*
90.1	CARLISLE	90.01	—
8.6	Gretna Junc	10.20	69/66
14.5	Mp14½	—	57¼
22.0	Mp22	—	68½/61
25.8	Lockerbie	26.20	75
33.5	Mp33½	—	71
35.5	Mp35½	—	74
39.7	Beattock	38.02	63½
45.4	Greskine Sdg	44.57	34
49.7	Beattock Summit	53.39	30
—	Lamington	—	75
66.9	Symington	68.30	69½/75
73.5	Carstairs	74.15	71½/75/35*
75.8	Lanark Junc	77.34	49½
—	Craigenhill	—	54
84.0	Law Junc	85.31	74/60*
87.6	Shieldmuir Junc	88.47	68
89.4	MOTHERWELL	91.22	—
4.5	Uddingston	5.37	70
6.3	Newton	7.27	60*
8.9	Rutherglen Junc	9.56	64
—	Eglinton Street	13.57	25*
12.9	GLASGOW CENTRAL	16.39	—

* Permanent speed restriction.

139

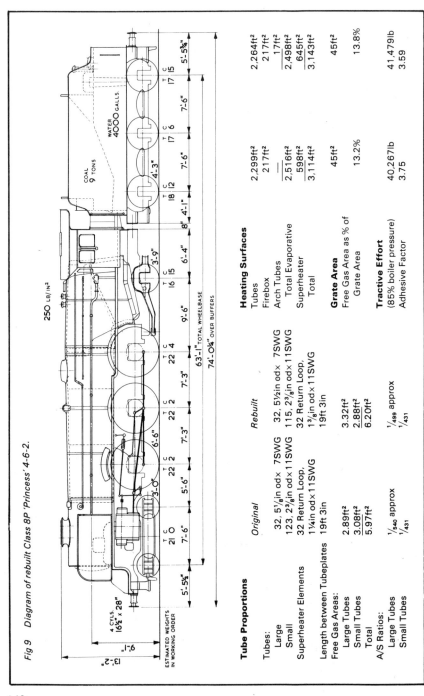

Fig 9   Diagram of rebuilt Class 8P 'Princess' 4-6-2.

Tube Proportions

	Original	Rebuilt
Tubes:		
Large	32, 5⅛in od × 7SWG	32, 5½in od × 7SWG
Small	123, 2⅜in od ×11SWG	115, 2⅜in od ×11SWG
Superheater Elements	32 Return Loop, 1¼in od×11SWG	32 Return Loop, 1⅜in od×11SWG
Length between Tubeplates	19ft 3in	19ft 3in
Free Gas Areas:		
Large Tubes	2.89ft²	3.32ft²
Small Tubes	3.08ft²	2.88ft²
Total	5.97ft²	6.20ft²
A/S Ratios:		
Large Tubes	1/540 approx	1/499 approx
Small Tubes	1/431	1/431

Heating Surfaces

Tubes	2,299ft²	2,264ft²
Firebox	217ft²	217ft²
Arch Tubes	—	17ft²
Total Evaporative	2,516ft²	2,498ft²
Superheater	598ft²	645ft²
Total	3,114ft²	3,143ft²

Grate Area

Grate Area	45ft²	45ft²
Free Gas Area as % of Grate Area	13.2%	13.8%

Tractive Effort

(85% boiler pressure)	40,267lb	41,479lb
Adhesive Factor	3.75	3.59

Apart from this, the only substantial changes would have been the use of roller bearings on all axles, the fitting of a multiple valve regulator in the superheater header, and the modification of the rear end of the frames, together with trailing truck and ashpan, on the same lines as Nos 46256/7. Married to coal-pusher tenders off 'Duchesses' — the stokers on the latter would have made the pushers superfluous—they would have been transformed into first-class machines. Fig 9 gives a diagram and important dimensions and ratios, while the new tubeplate layouts are shown in Fig 10.

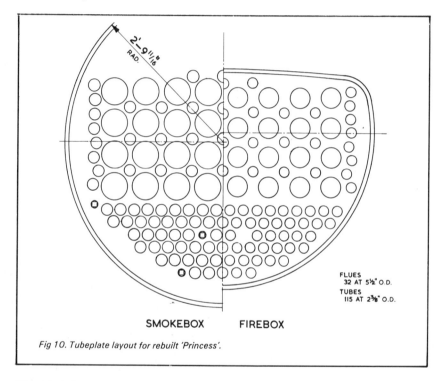

FLUES
32 AT 5½" O.D.
TUBES
115 AT 2⅜" O.D.

SMOKEBOX   FIREBOX

Fig 10. Tubeplate layout for rebuilt 'Princess'.

The 'Jubilees' (45552-45742*)

In rebuilding these as Class 7P 4-6-2s, there was a boiler ready made for the job; I refer to the 'Britannia' BR1 standard design. With a grate area of 42sq ft and well proportioned, it offered scope for a three-cylinder locomotive to keep within a maximum axleload of 21tons. And the combination of the 17in cylinders of the 'Jubilees' — at least the outside ones, because the inside one would need renewing to suit the larger smokebox saddle diameter — with 250lb/sq in boiler pressure behind them, had already been proved an excellent basis for a heavy passenger

*less two locomotives rebuilt to Class 7P 4-6-0s

141

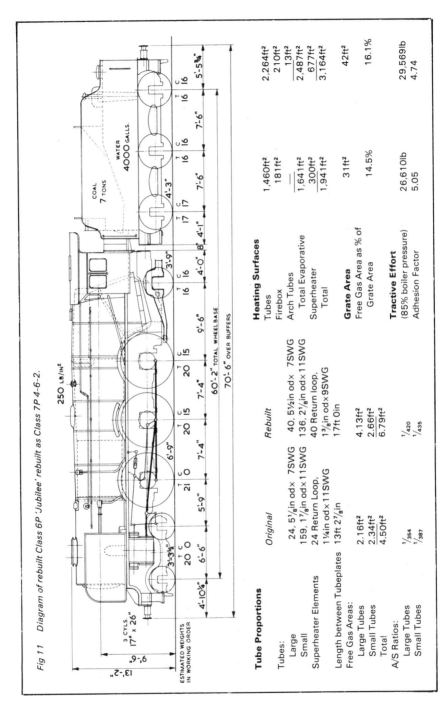

Fig 11   Diagram of rebuilt Class 6P 'Jubilee' rebuilt as Class 7P 4-6-2.

Tube Proportions

	Original	Rebuilt
Tubes:		
Large	24, 5⅛in od × 7SWG	40, 5½in od × 7SWG
Small	159, 1⅞in od × 11SWG	136, 2⅛in od × 11SWG
Superheater Elements	24 Return Loop, 1¼in od × 11SWG	40 Return loop, 1⅜in od × 9SWG
Length between Tubeplates	13ft 2⅞in	17ft 0in
Free Gas Areas:		
Large Tubes	2.16ft²	4.13ft²
Small Tubes	2.34ft²	2.66ft²
Total	4.50ft²	6.79ft²
A/S Ratios:		
Large Tubes	1/354	1/420
Small Tubes	1/387	1/435

Heating Surfaces

Tubes	2,264ft²	1,460ft²
Firebox	210ft²	181ft²
Arch Tubes	13ft²	—
Total Evaporative	2,487ft²	1,641ft²
Superheater	677ft²	300ft²
Total	3,164ft²	1,941ft²

Grate Area

	42ft²	31ft²
Free Gas Area as % of Grate Area	16.1%	14.5%

Tractive Effort

(85% boiler pressure)	29,569lb	26,610lb
Adhesion Factor	4.74	5.05

locomotive on the rebuilt 'Patriots' and the two 'Jubilee' rebuilds with the 2A boiler.

Fig 11 shows the diagram and dimensions of the design. The bogie, coupled wheels, outside cylinders and motion would be re-used, together with most of the frame stretchers other than the dragbox. New frames would have the slab section at the rear, à la 46256/7, with the standard cast steel trailing truck to match, while all such components as brake gear would be re-used. New spring gear with cottered tension links would be fitted to coupled wheels. The style is very much LM late-1940s, and makes quite a handsome engine. Use of these machines on the Midland expresses would have given scope for either heavier loads at existing 'XL limit' timings, or some acceleration with existing loads. Equally, they could have taken over the Euston-Birmingham trains, and calculations based on a water rate of 24,000lb/hr (steam rate 25,400lb/hr and coal rate 3,140lb/hr, for the 'Britannia' boiler) show that a running time of 83½min for the 94.0miles from Euston to Coventry would have been well within their capabilities with trains of 350tons tare. Details of such

Table 3. Euston-Coventry

Locomotive: Class 7P rebuilt 'Jubilee' 4-6-2.
Steam rate — 25,400lb/h with exhaust injector.
Load: 350 tons tare, 385 tons gross.

Distance		Running Time m.s.	Speeds m.p.h.
0.0	EUSTON	0.00	—
1.1	Camden No 1	—	25
5.4	Willesden Junc	8.53	59
7.0	Mp7	—	63½
14.2	Mp14¼	—	64½
17.5	Watford Junc	20.01	70½
31.7	Tring	32.12	71/70
40.2	Leighton Buzzard	—	83/80*
46.7	Bletchley	43.22	82/81
52.4	Wolverton	—	84/80*
59.9	Roade	53.31	70½
62.8	Blisworth	55.54	78½
69.7	Weedon	61.06	77½
76.6	Kilsby Tunnel South	—	72
82.6	RUGBY	71.48	79/45*
—	Brandon	—	75
94.0	COVENTRY	83.36	—

* Permanent speed restriction.

running are shown in Table 3. With 4% recovery margin, a timing of 86½min would have been perfectly realistic, representing an average speed of 65.2mph. For practical timetabling purposes these timings are largely identical with those for the 'Duchess' on a 510ton train, thus permitting a new uniformity of running for a whole service such as we have become accustomed to since electrification.

A small point worthy of mention: the Stanier 4,000gallon tender is shown to have its coal bunker capacity reduced from 9tons to 7, by fitting a steeper slope sheet at the rear, and moving the back bulkhead forward. This reflects the normal mileage to be run between coaling plant visits, and the wish to avoid the gradual build-up of old dross at the back which was hardly ever used or cleared, but caused trouble if it did reach the shovel.

Heavy Class 7P9F 2-8-2 Mixed Traffic Locomotive

Intended for the BR standard range was a heavy 2-8-2, as has been seen in the preceding chapter, and the reasons for not proceeding with it have been examined. This abandonment was a great pity, for such an engine could have fulfilled a valuable role in handling fast fitted freight on certain main lines where traffic was heavy or the road difficult. Again, the basis would be the 'Britannia' boiler, matched with the 20in by 28in 'Britannia' cylinder, (some modification to reduce the clearance volume was required), but using components from the mediocre Stanier 2-6-0s — the pony truck, 5ft 6in coupled wheels, numerous frame components, and the like. Again, the back end frames and trailing truck would follow the pattern set by Nos 46256/7. The motion would necessarily be new, and would follow LM practice in construction of expansion link, return crank mounting, and crosshead rather than that of the BR standard design. The standard 4,000gallon tender taken from Class 8F 2-8-0s would be fitted: the 2-8-0s in turn would have taken 3,500gallon Fowler tenders from withdrawn locomotives. Fig 12 shows the diagram and major dimensions.

Small Class 6P7F 2-8-2 Mixed Traffic Locomotive

The total weight of the big 2-8-2 would not make it universally usable over the system, particularly on some of the Scottish lines. But the adhesion, boiler power and sheer ability to pull of a 2-8-2 would be of great value on many such lines. There was a case, therefore, for a light 2-8-2 mixed traffic locomotive which could take over the tasks which were at the top of the Class 5's range or just beyond it. One thinks of the Perth-Inverness and Oban roads, the gruelling climbs between Ayr and Stranraer, the Peak Forest and other lines of the Midland, and the Manchester-Carlisle fitted freights via Blackburn and Hellifield. And

144

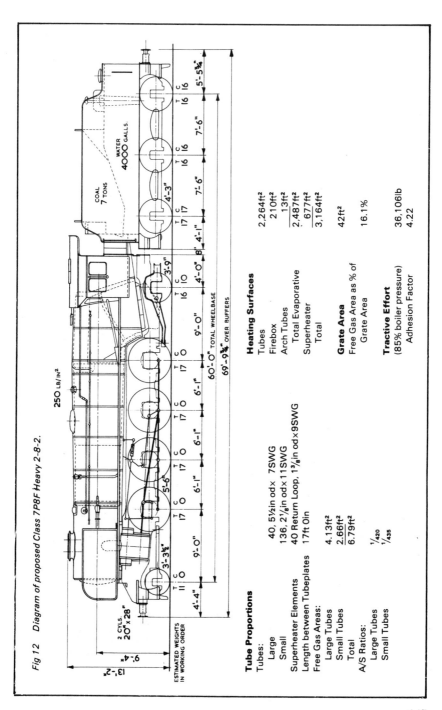

Fig 12 Diagram of proposed Class 7P8F Heavy 2-8-2.

Tube Proportions

Tubes:
Large   40, 5½in od × 7SWG
Small   136, 2⅛in od × 11SWG
Superheater Elements   40 Return Loop, 1³/₈in od × 9SWG
Length between Tubeplates   17ft 0in
Free Gas Areas:
Large Tubes   4.13ft²
Small Tubes   2.66ft²
Total   6.79ft²
A/S Ratios:
Large Tubes   ¹/₄₂₀
Small Tubes   ¹/₄₃₅

Heating Surfaces

Tubes   2,264ft²
Firebox   210ft²
Arch Tubes   13ft²
Total Evaporative   2,487ft²
Superheater   677ft²
Total   3,164ft²

Grate Area

    42ft²
Free Gas Area as % of
Grate Area   16.1%

Tractive Effort
(85% boiler pressure)   36,106lb
Adhesion Factor   4.22

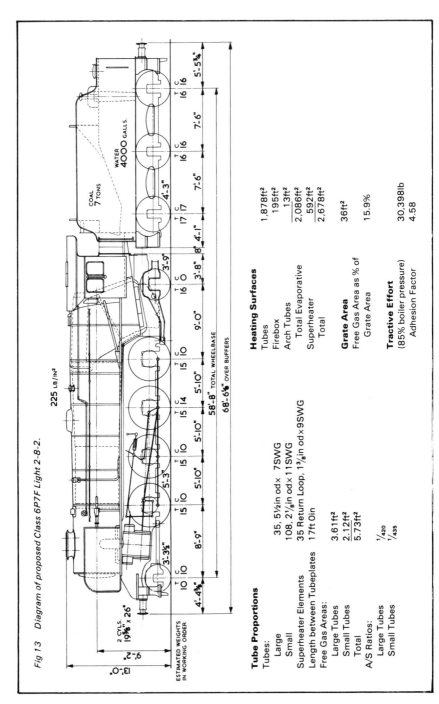

Fig 13   Diagram of proposed Class 6P7F Light 2-8-2.

Tube Proportions

Tubes:

Large	35, 5½in od × 7SWG
Small	108, 2⅛in od × 11SWG
Superheater Elements	35 Return Loop, 1⅜in od × 9SWG
Length between Tubeplates	17ft 0in

Free Gas Areas:

Large Tubes	3.61ft²
Small Tubes	2.12ft²
Total	5.73ft²

A/S Ratios:

Large Tubes	¹⁄₄₂₀
Small Tubes	¹⁄₄₃₅

Heating Surfaces

Tubes	1,878ft²
Firebox	195ft²
Arch Tubes	13ft²
Total Evaporative	2,086ft²
Superheater	592ft²
Total	2,678ft²

Grate Area

	36ft²
Free Gas Area as % of Grate Area	15.9%

Tractive Effort

(85% boiler pressure)	30,398lb
Adhesion Factor	4.58

what a boon at summer weekends for 10 or 12 coaches to Scarborough, Blackpool or Llandudno.

Again a BR standard boiler would have been used, this time the smaller 225 lb/sq in BR2 type used on the 'Clans'. It was of good proportions, its 36sq ft grate, ideal for such a locomotive, and the maximum axleloads with it could have been limited to 16tons. A double chimney would have overcome the shyness of this boiler on the 'Clans'.

Again, one looks round for standard LM components or salvageable material from unsatisfactory designs in producing a chassis for this boiler. First, there were the 5ft 3in coupled wheels of the Stanier 2-6-2 tanks, together with leading bissel truck. The frame back end would have followed the emerging standard pattern of slab extensions and the cast steel trailing truck. The most suitable 26in stroke cylinders to go on these frames would have been the $19\frac{5}{8}$in diameter ones of the 2-6-4 tanks; new motion would have been required. Fig 13 shows the diagram of this engine, also fitted with the 4,000-gallon, 7ton Stanier tender.

Heavy Class 5MT 2-8-4T Locomotive
The 2-6-4 tank, fine engine that it was, could hardly give rapid acceleration on some of the steeply graded commuter lines. One immediately thinks of such routes as Birmingham-Lichfield, Manchester Victoria-Oldham, and the Cathcart Circle, and there were others, all of which carried heavy traffic. For such work, eight-coupled wheels were really essential — and 5ft 3in diameter was ample.

The design in Fig 14, therefore, takes a number of available components and assembles them into a locomotive for this type of work. The frames are, of course, new, but take the 5ft 3in wheels and leading truck from the wretched Fowler 2-6-2 tanks together with redundant bogies from 2-6-4 tanks; some chassis material might be useable again. The cylinders would be the $19\frac{5}{8}$in by 26in ones of the 2-6-4 tanks; with new motion. The boiler is the early Class 5 type displaced by the use of chassis material for the Garratt design, and fitted with dome regulator. Tanks and bunker generally follow the lines of the 2-6-4 tanks, the capacities of 2,200gallons and 3tons being fully adequate for the work envisaged.

Class 4MT 2-6-0 Tender Locomotives (Rebuilt from 2-6-4Ts Nos 42300-42424, etc).
The Fowler parallel-boiler 2-6-4 tanks could have continued to play a useful role as tender engines following their progressive displacement from passenger work as a result of electrification schemes. Indeed, some of the earlier Stanier 2-6-4 tanks in the 424xx & 425xx series might well have been dealt with in the same way. Fig 15 is illustrative of the parallel boiler engines dealt with in this way, taking Fowler 3,500gallon tenders from withdrawn Class 2P 4-4-0s or Class 7F 0-8-0s. Tender cabs would be

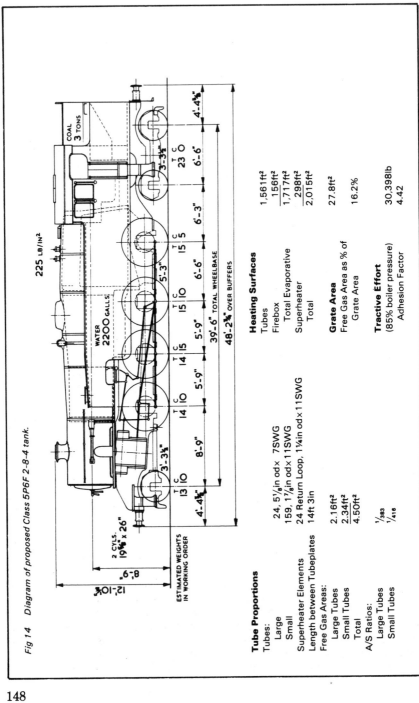

Fig 14   Diagram of proposed Class 5P6F 2-8-4 tank.

225 LB/IN²

COAL 3 TONS

WATER 2200 GALLS.

2 CYLS. 19⅝" x 26"

ESTIMATED WEIGHTS IN WORKING ORDER

4'-4¾" 8'-9" 5'-9" 5'-9" 6'-6" 6'-3" 6'-6" 4'-4¾"

3'-3¼"

T C 13 10   T C 14 10   T C 14 15   T C 15 10   T C 15 5   3'-3¼"   T C 23 0

39'-6" TOTAL WHEELBASE

48'-2¾" OVER BUFFERS

12'-10½"

6'-9"

Tube Proportions

Tubes:
Large   24, 5⅛in od × 7SWG
Small   159, 1⅞in od × 11SWG
Superheater Elements   24 Return Loop, 1¼in od × 11SWG
Length between Tubeplates   14ft 3in

Free Gas Areas:
Large Tubes   2.16ft²
Small Tubes   2.34ft²
Total   4.50ft²

A/S Ratios:
Large Tubes   1/383
Small Tubes   1/416

Heating Surfaces

Tubes   1,561ft²
Firebox   156ft²
Total Evaporative   1,717ft²
Superheater   298ft²
Total   2,015ft²

Grate Area   27.8ft²
Free Gas Area as % of
Grate Area   16.2%

Tractive Effort
(85% boiler pressure)   30,398lb
Adhesion Factor   4.42

148

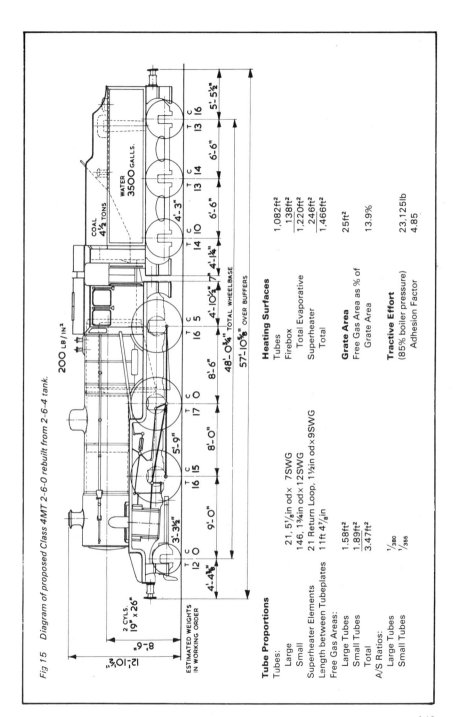

Fig 15 Diagram of proposed Class 4MT 2-6-0 rebuilt from 2-6-4 tank.

Tube Proportions

Tubes:
Large   21, 5$\frac{1}{8}$in od × 7SWG
Small   146, 1$\frac{3}{4}$in od × 12SWG
Superheater Elements   21 Return Loop, 1$\frac{1}{2}$in od × 9SWG
Length between Tubeplates   11ft 4$\frac{7}{8}$in

Free Gas Areas:
Large Tubes   1.58ft²
Small Tubes   1.89ft²
Total   3.47ft²

A/S Ratios:
Large Tubes $\frac{1}{380}$
Small Tubes $\frac{1}{355}$

Heating Surfaces

Tubes   1,082ft²
Firebox   138ft²
Total Evaporative   1,220ft²
Superheater   246ft²
Total   1,466ft²

Grate Area   25ft²
Free Gas Area as % of
Grate Area   13.9%

Tractive Effort
(85% boiler pressure)   23,125lb
Adhesion Factor   4.85

149

fitted in view of the need for some tender-first running on freight trips. The brake force would be nearly doubled by this rebuild.

The Compounds (40900-40939, 41085-41199)

One wonders whether there would have been any residual need for assistant engines on passenger trains if all the above programme had been implemented. This might well have been dependent on the degree to which acceleration produced increased demand and this was met by increased loadings, rather than by running more trains. I suspect there would always have been some requirement for assisting, and with a reducing locomotive fleet it might have been necessary (as was done in practice) to look round at all that was available for the purpose and make the best of it. This promptly brings the left-hand-drive Compounds into the limelight: relatively modern engines, with reasonable boilers having plenty of life left in them, the chassis was so appalling that a major rebuild would have been necessary to make them satisfactory. It is probable that not even all the LMS left-hand drive engines would have been needed for such work, permitting the early scrapping of the rest.

On this basis, Fig 16 shows a scheme for a moderate rebuilding of the Compounds to fit them for this role. The new frames would take side bolster bogies from the Stanier 2-6-4 tanks, converted to tender engines, and the old coupled wheels (re-axled and with some respectable axleboxes to them) but with two outside cylinders only, the $19\frac{5}{8}$in by 26in type of the 2-6-4 tanks being used with mainly new motion — though one would hope to reuse coupling and connecting rods. On top, the existing boiler would be used unaltered, but with a circular smokebox sitting on a proper saddle. Only the footframing and splashers would need adaptation to suit the cylinders and outside Walschaerts gear. The nominal tractive effort would be reduced slightly by this rebuild, but nobody could doubt that the power available at the tender drawbar would have been increased.

Class 4F 0-6-0 Tender Engines (44207-44606)

These engines were far too numerous to scrap and far too unsatisfactory to leave alone, even for their freight tasks. Again, an approach rather like that for the Compounds would have seemed appropriate, providing, in effect, new chassis but leaving the existing boiler and other components as far as possible untouched.

To make the axlebox bearings of adequate size, it was necessary to get away from the tyranny of the four eccentrics for the Stephenson valve gear, which pushed the cylinders apart and thus restricted the space between crank web and wheel boss. This could be done after a fashion using inside Walschaerts gear, although on the Class 7F 0-8-0s this did not produce better axle journals. A better proposition would appear to be to split the Walschaerts gear, leaving combination lever and expansion link between the frames, but giving an outside return crank drive to the

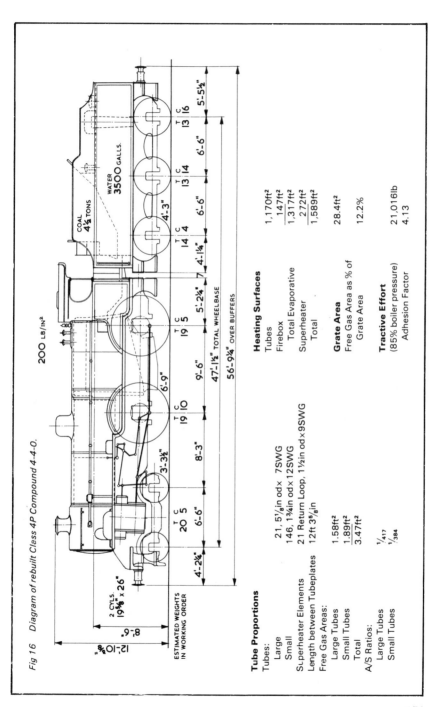

Fig 16   Diagram of rebuilt Class 4P Compound 4-4-0.

200 LB/IN²

2 CYLS.
19⅝" x 26"

WATER 3500 GALLS.

COAL 4½ TONS

ESTIMATED WEIGHTS IN WORKING ORDER

	T	C
20	5
19	10
19	5
14	4
13	14
13	16

4'-2¼" 6'-6" 3'-3½" 8'-3" 6'-9" 9'-6" 5'-2¼" 4'-1¼" 6'-6" 6'-6" 5'-5½"

47'-1½" TOTAL WHEELBASE

56'-9¼" OVER BUFFERS

8'-6"

12'-10⅝"

Tube Proportions

Tubes:
Large   21, 5⅛in od× 7SWG
Small   146, 1¾in od×12SWG
Superheater Elements   21 Return Loop, 1½in od×9SWG
Length between Tubeplates   12ft 3⅝in

Free Gas Areas:
Large Tubes   1.58ft²
Small Tubes   1.89ft²
Total   3.47ft²

A/S Ratios:
Large Tubes   1/417
Small Tubes   1/384

Heating Surfaces

Tubes   1,170ft²
Firebox   147ft²
Total Evaporative   1,317ft²
Superheater   272ft²
Total   1,589ft²

Grate Area

    28.4ft²

Free Gas Area as % of
Grate Area   12.2%

Tractive Effort

(85% boiler pressure)   21,016lb
Adhesion Factor   4.13

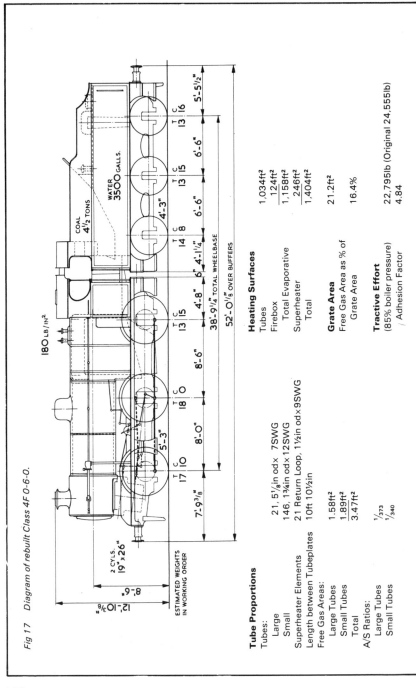

Fig 17 Diagram of rebuilt Class 4F 0-6-0.

180 LB/IN²

2 CYLS.
19" x 26"

ESTIMATED WEIGHTS
IN WORKING ORDER

WATER 3500 GALLS.

COAL 4½ TONS

Tube Proportions

Tubes:
Large   21, 5¹⁄₈in od × 7SWG
Small   146, 1¾in od × 12SWG
Superheater Elements   21 Return Loop, 1½in od × 9SWG
Length between Tubeplates   10ft 10½in
Free Gas Areas:
Large Tubes   1.58ft²
Small Tubes   1.89ft²
Total   3.47ft²
A/S Ratios:
Large Tubes   ¹⁄₃₇₃
Small Tubes   ¹⁄₃₄₀

Heating Surfaces

Tubes   1,034ft²
Firebox   124ft²
Total Evaporative   1,158ft²
Superheater   246ft²
Total   1,404ft²

Grate Area   21.2ft²

Free Gas Area as % of
Grate Area   16.4%

Tractive Effort
(85% boiler pressure)   22,795lb (Original 24,555lb)
Adhesion Factor   4.84

expansion link through a shaft. With this layout the cylinders could have been put as close together as the cover flanges would allow, and the piston valves as far apart as possible, the combination lever and link being between the connecting rods and the frame, and readily accessible from outside. This layout would be helped by reducing the cylinder diameter from 20in to 19in: the pressure would have been stepped up to 180lb/sq in (as on the Class 2P 4-4-0s with the same G7S boiler) to partly compensate. By these means the crank axle journals could have been increased in length, giving adequate bearing surfaces and freedom from hot boxes. New coupling rods would have been needed to suit the bigger crankpins to take the return cranks on the driving wheels, thus allowing the remaining pins to be increased in diameter and overcome the breakage problem referred to in Chapter 4. Fig 17 shows the diagram.

Class 3F 0-6-0 Shunting Tanks (47260-47681)

I have not said anything about these engines hitherto. They did the job they were asked to do well enough, but they did not offer their crews much protection, and coal capacity was rather deficient for the more continuous shunting turns. In addition, the axleboxes and motion were to old Midland standards and were very rackety at the higher mileages.

One wonders whether a case might have been made (it would have had to be based, probably, on the elimination of all intermediate repairs between general overhauls) for a modest rebuild of the chassis, using a geared, enclosed engine, rather after the Sentinel style, but horizontally disposed and nose-suspended, driving the intermediate axle. This should have been capable of running for the full boiler overhaul period (7 years maximum) without opening up.

Fig 18 shows what the resulting animal might have looked like, the opportunity having been taken to improve cab and bunker at the same time.

This, then would have been my comprehensive programme for adapting the LM locomotive fleet to the anticipated conditions of the second half of the twentieth century. I would not have envisaged steam lasting significantly longer than it did in fact do: it could not stand up on any economic grounds to the challenge of electrification or a properly developed diesel traction fleet. But a stud of the nature outlined would have enabled the service standards of the LM Region to be improved appreciably, both as planned in the timetable and in the actual execution day-to-day: it would have been much better able to combat the serious decline in standards of firing, coal quality and maintenance which developed as the preoccupation with dieselisation grew. It would have provided a degree of elbow-room, in terms of years, for dieselisation to be approached in an unhurried manner with proper development work to get a reliable machine before mass building took place. With hindsight, it would have been money well invested.

But the author remembers an episode in 1950 or thereabouts that

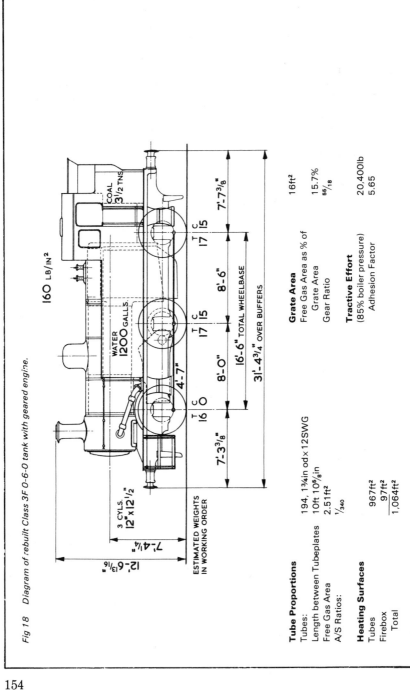

Fig 18   Diagram of rebuilt Class 3F 0-6-0 tank with geared engine.

160 LB/IN²

COAL 3½ TNS

WATER 1200 GALLS

3 CYLS. 12"×12½"

7'-4¼"

12'-6¹³/₁₆"

ESTIMATED WEIGHTS IN WORKING ORDER

T C 16 0

T C 17 15

T C 17 15

T C 17 15

7'-3³/₈"

8'-0"

8'-6"

7'-7³/₈"

4'-7"

16'-6" TOTAL WHEELBASE

31'-4³/₄" OVER BUFFERS

Tube Proportions

Tubes:	194, 1¾in od×12SWG
Length between Tubeplates	10ft 10⁵/₈in
Free Gas Area	2.51ft²
A/S Ratios:	¹/₃₄₀

Heating Surfaces

Tubes	967ft²
Firebox	97ft²
Total	1,064ft²

Grate Area

	16ft²
Free Gas Area as % of Grate Area	15.7%
Gear Ratio	⁵⁵/₁₈

Tractive Effort

(85% boiler pressure)	20,400lb
Adhesion Factor	5.65

154

suggests that it could not have happened. The Institution of Locomotive Engineers showed a film of the (then) new steam locomotive servicing arrangements installed by the Norfolk and Western Railroad in the USA. These were designed to dispose and reprepare the big J-class 4-8-4s and A and Y6b-class articulateds in just over an hour, including external cleaning, greasing, etc, which allowed the operating authorities to diagram the engines for 2hr turnrounds, not from shed inlet to outlet signal, but from station arrival to station departure. It was all put over with typical US panache and drive, a little clock in the corner of the picture recording the passage of time as two locomotives, a J and an articulated, went through the various stages. The whole thing was extremely stimulating as a record of what was being done many times a day in a number of depots. And what was the reaction of the large numbers of eminent British locomotive engineers present? They laughed!